The Pocket Encyclopaedia of
PLANT GALLS
IN COLOUR

The Pocket Encyclopaedia of

PLANT GALLS

IN COLOUR

Revised Edition

By

ARNOLD DARLINGTON
M.A., M.B.O.U., F.I.Biol.

The Biology Department, Malvern College, Worcestershire

with illustrations by

M. J. D. HIRONS

BLANDFORD PRESS
POOLE   DORSET

© 1968 Blandford Press Ltd.
Revised edition © 1975
Blandford Press Ltd,
Link House, West Street,
Poole, Dorset BH15 1LL

ISBN 0 7137 0748 8

Colour printed in Great Britain by Jarrold and Sons, Ltd., Norwich
and text printed by Fletcher & Son Ltd, Norwich
Bound by Richard Clay (The Chaucer Press) Ltd, Bungay, Suffolk

CONTENTS

Introduction	9
Galls: Their Cause and Variety	13
Gall Occupants and How They Live	18
Practical Work	26
Notes on the Illustrations	31
Illustrations	32
Representative British Galls	113
Index	185

DEDICATION

To those boys of Bishop's Stortford College
and Malvern College
who sought and obtained
much of the material for the
illustrations in this book.

\

INTRODUCTION

The Purpose of the Book

The present work sets out to do three things:

1. Provide a means of identification by summarizing the field characters of those types of plant galls which are likely to be found fairly easily;

2. Outline the mode of life of the principal gall-causing agents and some of their relationships with other organisms;

3. Suggest investigations which can be carried out in the field, the laboratory or at home, into the biology of galls.

References

Literature on galls, although extensive, consists mainly of papers on special aspects of the subject scattered through a wide range of scientific publications and requiring diligent, time-consuming research by the student. Examples of such papers include

Blair, K. G. 'Inhabitants of the rose bedeguar gall.' *Entomologists' Monthly Magazine*, 1943; **79,** 231–3; *Proceedings of the Royal Entomological Society*, 1945; **20,** 26–30.

Carleton, M. 'The bean-gall saw-fly.' *Journal of the Linnean Society, Zoology*, 1939; **11,** 575–624.

Folliot, R. 'Sur la reproduction de Diastrophus rubi Hartig.' *C.R. Acad. Sci., Paris*, **251,** 2597–8.

Salt, G. 'Phragmites and Lipara.' *School Science Review*, nos. 106, 107.

Went, F. W. 'On defence reactions in plants.' *American Naturalist*, 1940, **74,** 107–16.

There are also books dealing solely and thoroughly with particular groups of causers. Thus Barnes, H. F. (1951), *Gall Midges of Economic Importance*, Crosby, Lockwood & Son, summarizes, in effect, all the basic features of this order of insect cecidozoa.

Students wishing to identify the insect causers themselves will neglect at their peril the excellent check-lists published by the Royal

Entomological Society of London. One example is Eady, R. D., and Quinlan, J. (1963), *Hymenoptera (Cynipoidea) : key to families and subfamilies and Cynipinae (including galls)*. Handbooks for the identification of British insects, Vol. VIII, Part 1 (*a*), *Royal Entomological Society (London)*.

This lists all the gall-wasps recorded from the British Isles and is illustrated with line drawings.

Any work on a group of organisms whose members include gall-inducing species is likely to contain references which are more or less useful. One instance is the general review of insect life,

Imms, A. D. (1947), *Insect Natural History*. Collins.

Here a special chapter is effectively devoted to gall insects, in which examples are given of the various orders responsible for the formations and of those which become components of a gall community after its initiation.

Many of the earlier books intended to provide full coverage have long been out of print and, though still useful today, are old-fashioned in their illustrative techniques and include factual mistakes some of which were unavoidable at the time they were written. Four titles are

Connold, E. T. (1901), *British Vegetable Galls*, London: (1908), *British Oak Galls*, London: (1909), *Plant Galls of Great Britain*, London.

Swanton, E. W. (1912), *British Plant Galls*, London.

The investigator who intends to study cecidia in detail is well advised to consult the comprehensive monograph, Buhr, H. (1965), *Bestimmungstabellen der Gallen (Zoo- und Phytocecidien) an Pflanzen Mittel- und Nordeuropas*, Fischer (Jena), which is in two volumes and expensive, but copies are generally obtainable through the library services. A smaller work, published in English, is

Mani, M. S. (1964), *Ecology of plant galls*. Junk (The Hague).

This is essentially a précis of the main aspects of gall biology. Although of little use for identifications in the field, it contains a wealth of anatomical and physiological information and a comprehensive bibliography which presents the reader with the important literature relevant to his particular line of research.

All the publications listed above are among those consulted in the preparation of this book.

The Problem of Nomenclature

Hitherto, the taxonomy of many gall-causers has been so bedevilled by the confusing multiplicity of names that in certain groups (mites, for example) it is sometimes difficult to correlate the accounts of separate authors. This has arisen partly from a growing realization of the complexity of the situation and from the different —and changing—opinions of specialists about what constitute valid genera, species and subspecies. Until nomenclatural stability is attained, the naturalist will continue to be faced with a discouraging array of synonyms which add little to his understanding of the subject-matter. The general lack of popular names for any save the most conspicuous kinds only makes matters worse.

In this book an attempt has been made to attain a measure of simplicity consistent with reasonable precision and accuracy. It has been impossible to exclude all synonyms, since readers may wish to extend their studies to older works on particular aspects of gall natural history.

To minimize congestion in the headings to the sections, the author of each scientific name is given in the index only.

Acknowledgements

The author acknowledges, with gratitude, the advice he has received from Messrs L. E. Carey, J. B. Evans and J. G. Sheals of the Departments of Entomology, Botany and Zoology at the British Museum (Natural History); Dr Ann R. Sanderson of the University of St Andrews; and Mr Keith Harris of the Royal Horticultural Society's Garden at Wisley. Faults are those of the writer, not his advisers.

PREFACE TO THE SECOND EDITION

A new edition gives an opportunity for correcting errors of fact, conforming to alterations in scientific nomenclature, and noting changes in the status of organisms under review. The last hold surprises for the specialist and non-specialist alike: space has been found for particulars of several gall causers which, since the late

1960s, have become sufficiently conspicuous features of our flora and fauna to justify notice in a book of this kind.

The writer continues to be indebted to many correspondents for information and advice, painstakingly prepared and given ungrudgingly. Henry L. G. Stroyan of the Plant Pathology Laboratory at Harpenden has furnished an impressive mass of factual data about aphid cecidozoa; Thomas Kavanagh of the Agricultural Institute in Dublin has given an account of the new rust *Puccinia terrieriana*; and Margaret M. Hutchinson of Haslemere has kept constantly in touch over the new cola-nut gall and the various cynipids periodically infesting Turkey oak. To these observers must be added the scores of naturalists who, by their sightings of *Andricus quercus-calicis*, have enabled the extension of its range to be charted.

Arnold Darlington

5 Firs Close,
Malvern,
Worcestershire.
February 1975.

Illustrator's Acknowledgements

I wish to express my gratitude to all who have searched for, and provided specimens, especially the pupils of Bishop's Stortford College, Malvern College, my own students, Mr J. Quinlan of the Department of Entomology, British Museum (Natural History) and to my wife who has cared for all the living material received through the post until it could be used for illustrations.

To my son J. D. M. Hirons I am indebted for the photographs of the 'pit gall' *Asteriolecanium variolosum* on oak and the 'crown gall' on swede.

M. J. D. Hirons

Easthampstead Park College of Education,
Wokingham,
Berks.

GALLS: THEIR CAUSE AND VARIETY

Plant galls (cecidia) are so numerous, widespread and varied that most people are probably familiar with examples even if they do not understand their cause and sometimes confuse them with very different objects which, from time to time, appear on plants.

A gall arises as a result of parasitic attack. It represents the growth reaction of the host—a plant—to the attack of a parasite—a bacterium, fungus, eelworm, mite or insect—and develops either by an abnormal increase in the number of plant cells or by the cells becoming abnormally enlarged. This definition immediately excludes numerous deformities brought about by organisms—for example, foliage curled into cylindrical scrolls by caterpillars and secured by webbing; the black blotches like splashes of tar on sycamore leaves caused by the fungus *Rhytisma acerinum*; or most of the mines burrowed in the thickness of leaves by insect larvae (but see p. 125). Such are not galls because the role of the plant is passive, and it does not respond by growth to the attack. Examples of formations which might be confused with galls are illustrated on p. 33.

Whatever its form, a gall is derived wholly from the tissues of the host plant. In no sense is the parasite the gall-*maker*: it is the gall-*causer* and merely provides the stimulus for the localized growth of the plant. Almost invariably, gall formation is closely associated with the reproduction of the parasite.

The manner of stimulation differs among the various causers. The hymenopteran *Pontania proxima*, which galls willow foliage, evidently injects an irritant when her ovipositor pierces the leaf, since a gall sometimes develops around the site of the puncture even if an egg is not deposited. Most hymenopteran galls, however, fail to grow at all unless eggs are laid which hatch: in many, at least, of these the stimulus is evidently a substance secreted by the digestive glands of the feeding larvae. As soon as the insects stop feeding—when they pupate or if they die—their galls cease to develop further. Aphid galls of the genus *Pemphigus*, which form on the leaf-stalks of poplar, only begin to grow after the adult female has pierced the tissues with her beak and has started to suck their juices. Parasitic fungi may stimulate their hosts to form galls by secreting growth hormones, and such hormones have been detected in fungal cultures set up in the laboratory. Sometimes strange side-effects appear in addition to development localized at the actual site of infestation: when certain eelworms gall the roots of small scabious (*Scabiosa columbaria*), its flowers may become malformed. A great deal of interesting research remains to be done on the stimuli emitted by gall-causers and the problems furnish opportunities for amateurs and professionals alike.

Excluding viruses, the nature of which is obscure and which are doubtfully alive, the principal gall-causers infesting European land plants comprise five major groups of organisms, two of plants (cecidophyta) and three of animals (cecidozoa). Some of these are large enough to warrant further subdivision.

CECIDOPHYTA

1. *Bacteria*. Although individually the smallest and least impressive of the gall agents, the structures they induce may be large or relatively complex. Crown-galls of *Agrobacterium tumefaciens* vary greatly in size according to their environmental conditions and sometimes become enormous. Probably the best known bacterial galls are the small root-nodules on leguminous plants colonized by nitrogen-fixing bacteria of the genus *Rhizobium*. If sectioned and examined microscopically, such nodules are seen to be made up of several zones, each more or less specialized.

2. *Fungi*. The most important of the cecidophyta, covering many species of several different classes and infesting a wide range of hosts. The mycelial hyphae may pass between the host's cells or penetrate them by haustoria (absorptive organs), or there may be no real mycelium at all, as in *Synchitrium endobioticum* which causes the black-wart disease of potatoes. Some kinds undergo a sort of alternation of generations in that they infest two different host species during the course of the life-cycle (Fig. 3).

CECIDOZOA

3. *Nematoda* (round worms). The gall species belong to the order *Anguilluloidea* (eelworms) and are medium-sized nematodes well

adapted for parasitism, with the power of gall-induction particularly highly developed. Many species can survive for long periods in markedly adverse conditions away from their hosts.

4. *Acarina* (mites). Most of the gall-causers belong to the family *Eriophyidae* and are elongated, cylindrical mites, exceedingly small (often less than 0·1 mm long), blind, without respiratory or circulatory systems, and with the legs reduced to two pairs. The mouthparts are adapted for sucking liquid food from plants and, because of their minute size, eriophyids are generally capable of piercing single cells. Females are much more abundant than males and reproduction is commonly by parthenogenesis.

5. *Insecta*. These make up the majority of cecidozoa. Five orders are of importance.

(a) *Hemiptera–Homoptera* (bugs). Families *Aphidae* (green-flies), *Chermidae = Psyllidae* (jumping plant-lice) and *Coccidae* (scale insects). Galls induced by aphids include some of striking complexity. Alternation of generations (Fig. 2) always occurs, the aphids undergoing sexual, and various forms of asexual, reproduction in the process, and frequently alternating between a woody host in the winter and spring and a herbaceous host in the summer. Psyllids somewhat resemble aphids—the nymphs are flattened insects, usually covered with a waxy secretion, and are generally rather sluggish. Coccids are remarkable for striking difference between the two sexes. The female is a degenerate, sessile insect, which remains fixed in one place on a plant and feeds there, sometimes inducing a simple gall in that position. The males move about in search of the females.

(b) *Hymenoptera* (wasps, etc.). Five main families are involved in gall relationships: gall-causers only—*Tenthredinoidea* (sawflies); either gall-causers or inquilines ('lodgers') in existing gall tissues —*Cynipoidea* (gall-wasps); mostly parasites or predators on other gall occupants—*Chalcidoidea* (chalcid wasps), *Ichneumonidea* (ichneumon-flies) and *Braconidae* (supplementary ichneumon-flies).

Hymenoptera in general have two pairs of membranous wings, the hind pair being the smaller, with the wings of a side linked together by tiny hooks, and most of them have a well-defined waist. A sawfly has no waist and its ovipositor is modified to form a saw. Its larva lives in the gall and resembles the caterpillar of a moth, but it has only a single eye on each side of the head instead of a group of eyes and more legs (sawfly larva 9 or more pairs, caterpillar 8 pairs or less). Pupation is often in the soil. Cynipids are small, hard-bodied wasps whose legless larvae have biting mouthparts: they induce galls of complicated structure, usually on woody plants like oak and rose, and frequently undergo an alternation of asexual and sexual generations. They invariably pupate inside the gall. Chalcids are minute wasps, sometimes with a metallic sheen, which are easily recognized by the reduction of the venation to a single nervure along the front of the wing. Like the slimmer ichneumons and braconids, chalcids are mostly parasitic in other insects, although a few are true gall-causers.

(c) *Diptera* (two-winged flies). The chief gall-causers are the *Itonididae = Cecidomyiidae* (gall-midges), whose larvae feed and develop in more or less complex galls and pupate either in the galls themselves or in the soil. The adults do not feed. A few members of other dipterous families induce gall-formation.

(d) *Coleoptera* (beetles, including weevils).

(e) *Lepidoptera* (moths).

Larvae of several beetles and moths bring about the formation of galls in which they develop, but they are relatively unimportant compared with the first three insect orders.

The external features of typical gall-causers are shown on pp. 34–35.

THE CLASSIFICATION OF GALLS

Almost any organ in the aerial or subterranean systems of vascular plants can become galled by some agent or other, and the striking diversity of form exhibited by galls depends partly on the organ infested and partly on the agent. Galls can be classified in several ways: one of these is based on the position of the causative organism.

Causers may remain on the surface, more or less exposed, in the hollows of thickenings—*krebsgalls* (coccids, some aphids and many fungi); or among hairs growing in superficial patches—*filzgalls* (chiefly mites); become wrapped in the thickened, turned-over margin of a leaf-blade—*fold or roll galls* (mites, aphids, gall-midges, rarely hymenopterans); become enclosed in a cup, either very shallow or hemispherical, oval or conical, formed by the arching of one surface of the infested structure with the opposite surface following it and leaving an opening to the exterior—*pouch galls* (mainly mites, aphids and a few gall-midges). In all four, the causers are essentially outside the plant tissues. On the other hand, they may become completely embedded within the gall through its tissues rising up and concealing them—*covering galls* (mites, aphids and gall-midges); sink from the outside into a chamber formed by plant cells dissolving away and the aperture of the cavity subsequently closing—*lysenchyme galls* (gall-wasps only); be deep within the plant tissues from the very beginning of the gall's development —*mark galls* (some sawflies and gall-wasps). These can be subdivided into smaller groups. The most diverse and complex are the lysenchyme galls of cynipid wasps.

Grouping can also refer to the arrangement of the cecidozoa in their chambers within insect galls. A *unilocular* gall contains a single cavity and a *plurilocular* gall more than one: *unilarval* denotes the presence of a single insect in each cavity and *multilarval* more than one.

Galls on aerial structures have a general tendency to be pale at first and then to pass through a reddish phase, especially under the influence of light, before darkening to brown or black.

Like parasites in general, gall-causers tend to show a measure of specificity for certain hosts. Most gall-wasps, for example, are confined to oaks (*Quercus* spp.); of the minority, a large proportion occur on rosaceous plants. Sawflies of the genus *Pontania* only infest willows (*Salix* spp.); weevils of the genus *Gymnetron* the flowers and sometimes the roots, mainly of Scrophulariaceae; a closely related weevil, *Miarus*, is restricted to the flowers of Campanulaceae. Exceptions to this general rule of specificity include the crown-gall bacterium (*Agrobacterium tumefaciens*) and such eelworms as *Anguillulina dipsaci*, both of which can parasitize numerous species, many of them unrelated.

The hosts themselves are so diverse that representatives of all the plant phyla are galled, including such non-vascular forms as freshwater and marine algae, and also fungi, lichens and bryophytes. Here we are concerned only with terrestrial vascular plants.

GALL OCCUPANTS AND HOW THEY LIVE

THE GALL COMMUNITY

Besides the original causer, a variety of other organisms may colonize a gall, particularly if it is one of the larger kind, and set up a community of fascinating complexity.

Larvae of other insects, such as chalcid wasps, may live as *parasites* within the larvae or pupae of a causer and kill them. Normally, these parasites encompass the death of their host only when it is no longer to their disadvantage to do so—when they have completed their own feeding and are ready to disperse. In a sense, they can be regarded as highly specialized *predators* which budget well, instead of parasites which kill the goose that lays the golden eggs. These predator-parasites, in turn, may be attacked by parasites of their own, or *hyperparasites*—ichneumons and braconids, for example—which emerge from eggs laid by females able to seek out suitable hosts, even though such hosts are deeply concealed within the tissues of other animals.

Inquilines, including mites and the larvae of cynipid wasps, certain flies, beetles and small moths, may colonize the gall, dwelling as lodgers in the enlarged tissues and living as commensals with the actual causer and sharing its food, so that it may be adversely affected and even destroyed by starvation. In addition, small non-parasitic predators sometimes move in and devour the other occupants one by one; or the causers, inquilines and predators alike may be eaten by birds which either swallow the gall whole or break it open to reach them.

In some kinds of gall, such as that of the dipteron *Lasioptera rubi* on bramble, inception is due to an insect which devours the mycelium of a fungus growing and feeding on the galled tissues: in these cases, the parent insect may introduce the appropriate fungus at the time of egg-laying. Should the actual causer be a fungus, its activities sometimes pave the way for colonization by a fungus of another species (as in the *Albugo-Peronospora* gall). Whatever the nature of the causer, the gall it induces can be invaded and colonized by a range of *successori* both before and after all the

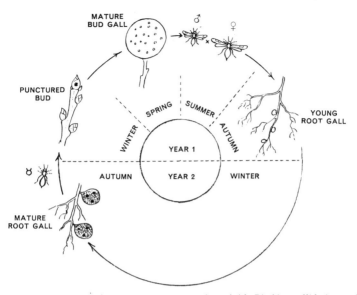

Fig. 1. Alternation of generations: 1 – an oak cynipid, *Biorhiza pallida* (p. 151).

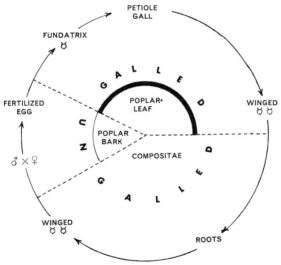

Fig. 2. Alternation of generations: 2 – a gall aphid, *Pemphigus bursarius* (p. 161).

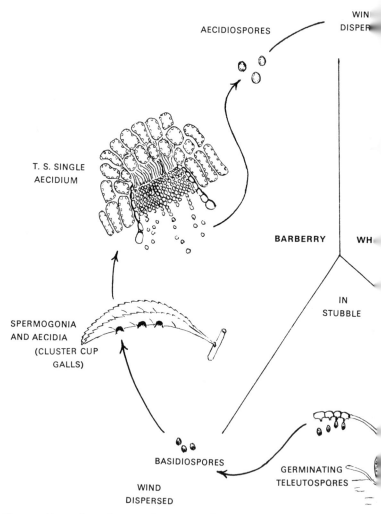

AECIDIOSPORES

WIN
DISPER

T. S. SINGLE
AECIDIUM

BARBERRY   WH

IN
STUBBLE

SPERMOGONIA
AND AECIDIA
(CLUSTER CUP
GALLS)

BASIDIOSPORES

WIND
DISPERSED

GERMINATING
TELEUTOSPORES

Fig. 3. Alternation of generations: 3 – a 'higher' fungus, *Puccinia graminis* (p. 116).

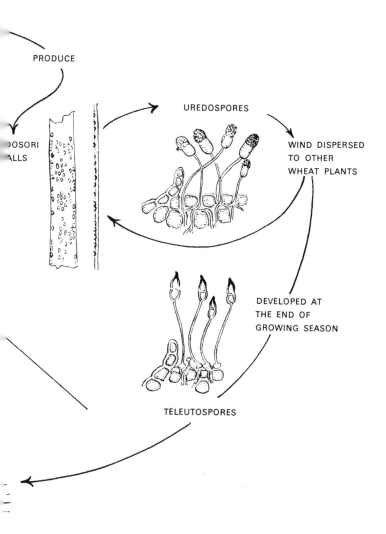

PRODUCE

UREDOSOSORI
WALLS

UREDOSPORES

WIND DISPERSED
TO OTHER
WHEAT PLANTS

DEVELOPED AT
THE END OF
GROWING SEASON

TELEUTOSPORES

early occupants have left. Most of these are small, although some
—like the house sparrow (*Passer domesticus*) and the jackdaw
(*Corvus monedula*), which have been known to establish nests in
old witches-broom growths—are surprisingly large. (Not all
witches-brooms are the result of parasitic attack, however—see
pl. 4). Despite the need for further work on the subject, successori
can be seen clearly to include organisms which are specific to
certain kinds of gall and not merely non-selective shelterers. The
term *casuals* is sometimes applied to these forms, but it is not
always suitable.

The relationships between one species and another in most gall
communities have been so little studied that they are either uncertain or unknown. Here, then, is a profitable field of inquiry for the
amateur who cares to collect, observe and breed out the various
occupants, even from the very commonest galls.

ALTERNATION OF GENERATIONS

Three main groups of gall-causing organisms—cynipid wasps,
aphids and fungi—include species which undergo what is sometimes termed *alternation of generations*. Its most precise form is seen in
some of the insects, when it involves two generations in the course of
the life-cycle (often within the span of a single year). One—the
agamic generation—consists exclusively of females; the other of individuals of both sexes. The bisexual generation gives rise to fertilized eggs normally laid towards the approach of winter and able to
withstand adverse conditions. From these, agamic females emerge
which lay parthenogenetic (unfertilized) eggs and such eggs, which
develop during milder conditions, produce the bisexual generation.

1. *Cynipids.* Many of the gall-wasps on oak pass through this
sort of life-history during which they induce two different galls to
form, considered by early observers to belong to separate species
and to which separate names are still applied by some naturalists
today. (The duplication and confusion partly account for the many
synonyms for these forms.) The over-wintering galls from which the
agamic females develop are frequently protected in some way: by
being established underground on the roots, for instance, or by
falling off the host plant so that they become blanketed by dead
foliage shed in autumn.

The females of either generation are invariably diploid (i.e. their chromosomes are present in pairs) and the males are haploid (only a single component of every chromosome pair is present). A female of the agamic generation receives the diploid condition from her two parents, since the egg from which she develops, and the male cell which fertilizes it, are each haploid. Such females appear to be, in effect, of two types: those laying diploid eggs only, which invariably yield females; and those producing exclusively haploid eggs which, since there is no fertilization, give rise solely to males. The haploid condition in these eggs arises during their formation within the parent's body by the number of chromosomes becoming halved.

The oak-apple cynipid, *Biorhiza pallida*, provides a typical example of such a cycle. On the other hand, there are gall-wasps whose males are rarely seen (e.g. *Diplolepis rosae*), or possibly are unnecessary (such as *Andricus kollari*). Apparently the last two represent a simplification of the basic life-cycle through suppression of the bisexual generation and their reproduction is normally or invariably by parthenogenesis.

2. *Aphids*. All aphids pass through a form of alternation, in which both unisexual and bisexual stages appear, but this invariably covers more than two clear-cut generations and frequently involves the colonization of two different host plants, woody and herbaceous. Typically, an aphid over-winters on a woody plant as a fertilized egg, from which a large, wingless female—the fundatrix or stem-mother—emerges in spring. She feeds on the tissues of the woody host, sometimes bringing about gall-formation in the process, and reproduces asexually, giving rise exclusively to females. Some of these, which are winged, may migrate to a herb where they feed without inducing galls, and where they produce a succession of generations asexually, the earlier of which consist solely of females. In autumn, on the approach of adverse conditions, a return is made to the woody plant: males appear as well as females, and the mating of the two sexes results in the over-wintering eggs which are normally laid in such sheltered places as bark crevices.

This form of life-history appears in *Pemphigus bursarius* which galls the leaf-stalks of poplar and alternates with a herbaceous composite. Gall-causing aphids exhibit a number of variations on this basic trend, however, and one of the hosts is sometimes omitted altogether. In the closely related *P. spirothecae*, colonization is restricted to poplar.

3. *Fungi.* These undergo various forms of alternation which correspond only in the most general sense to what happens in insects. For example, some 'lower' fungi (Phycomycetes) overwinter as a fertilized body (oospore) while reproducing in summer by propagules (conidia and zoospores) which arise asexually. They parasitize a single host. 'Higher' fungi, like many of the rusts (Basidiomycetes), have a more complex life-cycle, in which two hosts, both woody or one woody and the other herbaceous, are colonized in sequence, both of them galled, and several different sorts of reproductive body appear, one of which—the teleutospore —is typically a resting-stage adapted for surviving conditions such as cold or drought unfavourable for active metabolism. The aecidium stage is one of short duration when spores are successively produced and germinate immediately, while uredospores serve for the rapid spread of the parasite in summer. In the course of the life-cycle, a highly specialized form of sexual reproduction takes place, the minutiae of which are outside the scope of this book.

The rust *Coleosporium senecionis*, alternating between groundsel (teleutospore generation) and pine (aecidial generation), typifies the cycle in a higher fungus. With rusts, it is a broad, although not constant rule, that the uredospores and teleutospores occur on the herbaceous host and the aecidial stage on the woody host.

Alternation in the three groups is represented schematically on pp. 19–21.

EFFECTS ON THE HOST

The careful observer of gall infestation is likely to be impressed by two things: the widespread nature of the phenomenon and the fact that the relationship between host and parasite is so nicely balanced that mortal damage to the colonized plant is the exception rather than the rule. The view held by some naturalists, that parasitism is a condition highly injurious to the host, is demonstrably unsound. It is a common experience to see densely galled plants reproducing freely, and reproduction is the ultimate test of biological success. Nevertheless, the destruction of acorns by the cynipid *Andricus quercus-calicis* (p. 32, Fig. *a*) should be considered as an exception.

Clearly the host would be better off without its gall, since the relationship between the two operates predominantly in favour of the causer, which receives three things—shelter, a supply of food and a place wherein to breed. The plant, on the other hand, utilizes material in forming the gall which otherwise would be of value to its general metabolism. But most galls do, at least, isolate the parasite and tend to localize any toxins it may produce; and cases are known, like the nitrogen-fixing bacteria *Rhizobium radicicola* and *R. beyerinckii* in the root galls on leguminous plants, where the host derives some benefit from the relationship.

When these causers promote the welfare of their hosts, the beneficial effect seems to be incidental rather than inherent. Evidently what happens is that the quantity of organic matter synthesized by the host and removed by the causer is considerably greater than the immediate requirements of the latter, which has the power of combining free nitrogen in the soil air with the elements carbon, hydrogen and oxygen obtained from the host's carbohydrates, so that a simple protein (amino-compound) is formed. The excess amino-compounds become absorbed and assimilated by the host; but if the bacterium were not present, the legume would be perfectly capable of synthesizing protein for itself, when the nitrogen would come, not from the soil atmosphere but from nitrates dissolved in the soil water. The causer supplements protein synthesis by the host and, to some extent, enables it to take a short cut. The alternatives can be summarized as follows:

UNGALLED PLANT   GALLED PLANT

PRACTICAL WORK

Gall collecting is facilitated by the tendency of causers to colonize herbs and the lower levels of shrubs and young trees growing in relatively open situations (hedgerows and woodland margins). Only the simplest equipment is needed—secateurs and a supply of plastic bags in which to store the gathered material. For galls growing out of reach, a useful addition is a hooked walking-stick or a pair of long-handled pruning cutters. A lepidopterist's beating-tray, an open umbrella or a sheet spread on the ground, can be used to catch the dislodged specimens. For subterranean galls, a fern trowel is usually adequate, since most of the species infest roots just below the soil surface.

Despite the variety and widespread distribution of galls, some situations are more likely than others to support a large range. Profitable localities include lanes, or tracks alongside fields, both flanked by woods or neglected, overgrown hedgerows comprising dense scrub with a thick growth of herbaceous vegetation at the base. A similar region is old parkland, where self-sown trees and shrubs are allowed to survive and the grass to become weedy, with scything and pruning seldom carried out. Although causative organisms usually infest young growths, and cutting promotes an increase of new shoots, frequent removal of the apices destroys so many developing galls that the populations of the mature parasites may become significantly reduced.

From time to time, ornamental plants grown indoors become galled. One example is shown in Pl. 126.

For naturalists suitably equipped with talent and apparatus, probably the best way of recording finds is to photograph the galls in colour or to make coloured drawings of them. The scale should be noted in every case.

Preserving

Galled vegetation can usually be preserved like pressed herbarium material, although extreme flattening is clearly undesirable. If it is intended to make such a collection, the material must be allowed to dry out thoroughly before being stored. The less bulky galls can be filed away in transparent envelopes, either purchased ready-made or cut from plastic bags, and made airtight by sealing the open end with the point of a flat-iron or the edge of a flat strip of hot metal. A few crystals of paradichlorbenzene or naphthalene sealed in with the specimen are advisable as a precaution against destructive mites. Galls which are too thick to store in this way can be placed in boxes fitted with transparent covers of glass or plastic, and protected from mites as before.

One way of preserving the shape dimensionally is to place the specimen in a box, cover it with sand and then warm it gently in an oven until all the moisture has been withdrawn. The sand particles should then be removed carefully with a camel-hair brush. Material treated in this way becomes brittle and difficult to handle; but it can be stored and displayed in a box. Shapes are easier to retain than colours.

Alternatively, galls can be preserved in alcohol (7 parts of industrial spirit to 3 parts of water). The advantage here is that the gall tissues are preserved, together with those of any occupants: thus material is available for examination at a later period. Disadvantages include the removal in solution of pigments (chlorophyll, liptochrome, anthoxanthin, etc.), so that several changes of solution may be necessary before the gall is finally placed in position; and the bulk of the container (jar or specimen-tube) needed to accommodate it.

Whatever method is adopted, careful records should be kept and included with the specimen: the species, locality, date and the finder's name are essential.

Difficulties in setting and displaying the animal components of a gall community arise from their small size. Very few are large enough for pinning in the manner followed by lepidopterists (although, with care, this might be done with something like the beetle *Saperda populnea*). One effective way of dealing with small insects is to fix the freshly killed specimen to the tip of one corner of a triangular card in a minute drop of adhesive prepared by dissolving celluloid in amyl acetate until the liquid reaches a creamy consistency. The legs, wings and antennae are extended under a hand lens before the adhesive sets. The card is pinned to a cork in a box, the top and bottom of which are of glass to permit both dorsal and ventral surfaces of the specimen to be examined without disturbing it. Alternatively, cecidozoa can be preserved in tubes of alcohol or formalin, or mounted on microscope slides. Such material is of value only if relevant field data are recorded.

At present, there are few private or museum collections.

WORK WITH LIVING MATERIAL

The study of living galls gives opportunities for fresh discoveries, since our understanding of several aspects of their ecology remains incomplete. For example, little reliable information is available about the regional distribution of many of the species described here, including several which are conspicuous; or their local distribution within a particular region and some of the environmental factors—exposure to wind, sunlight, sea-spray, etc.—which may operate to control it. Again, the complex communities which frequently develop inside galls still require investigation, as do the successori which move in and colonize the structures after the primary occupants have left. Some problems can be investigated if galls are incubated indoors.

REARING AND CULTURING

Rearing gall occupants is one of the most rewarding pursuits. Hitherto, it has tended to be neglected by the amateur, although excellent work has been done on individual species, gall-wasps especially. Much remains to be learned about the conditions in which galls need to be kept to yield the best results so that, in the present state of our knowledge, the investigator must be prepared for difficulties and variable success.

In general, probably the best way of obtaining animal colonizers is to keep the galled structures in glass jars covered with fine-mesh fabric (not plastic jam-pot covers). The galls should be removed after the causers have ceased feeding, when separation from the host is unlikely to inhibit their development. Insect larvae inside galls which are gathered prematurely will either die, or, if possible, pupate, but any which survive will merely become undersized imagines. Unless soil is necessary for pupation, a layer of dry silver sand on the floor of the container is a useful absorbent for water issuing from the plant tissues and condensing on the glass. Some animal colonizers, however, seem definitely to need moisture. Many occupants with short life-histories which complete their development *in situ* emerge successfully from galled sprays enclosed in porous bags. Where the causers pupate in the ground, the galls can be placed on the surface of fine soil or leaf-mould in plant-pots fitted with mesh covers, and the substrate dampened periodically by the application of mist from a scent-spray or atomizer. A specimen-tube filled with water, its mouth loosely plugged with cotton-wool or protected by a mesh cover, and the whole inserted in the soil, is a useful means of maintaining a high humidity in the air within the pot.

Certain cecidozoa require the natural conditions to be imitated very closely. The unisexual generation of cynipids developing in spangle-galls on oak foliage normally emerge after the spangles have fallen to the ground and over-wintered beneath a protective layer of dead leaves. So well are the causers adapted to this mode of life that, although some may issue from spangles lying on dry sand, the yield is likely to be insignificant unless the natural surroundings are duplicated in such a way as to maintain damp conditions. The water is necessary for the expansion of the galls, which continues after their separation from the tree.

Experience alone will determine the most suitable situations in which to keep the galls. While a few colonizers require warmth and seem to be unharmed by direct sunlight in moderation—such, for example, as some hymenopterans which gall the outer parts of shrub and tree canopies—many do better in cooler, shadier conditions. Mites, in particular, tend to be adversely affected by heat but able to withstand remarkably low temperatures. For convenience, emergence of adult insects can frequently be delayed without injury if galls are placed for a time in a refrigerator.

A careful watch should be maintained for mould developing on the plant tissues, and this should be brushed off if and when it appears. Since some causers take two or more years to complete their life-cycle, cultures should not be discarded hastily.

In many cases, gall induction and development can be observed directly. For example, if oaks of three–four years' growth are reared in plant-pots, experimental breeding of the causers can be carried out, and this proves to be a most fascinating study, the alternating generations of some of the oak cynipids being especially interesting. Induction can be attempted by sleeving on plants growing in the open or in a greenhouse, the causers being enclosed in muslin bags tied round branches. Sleeving or caging of adult insects on plants is not particularly difficult, although it does require patience. Using gall-midges, the late Dr H. F. Barnes worked wonders in this field and maintained very large populations, both of adults and larvae, in his insectary.

NOTES ON
THE ILLUSTRATIONS

The illustrations in nearly every instance have been made from living material and photographed on colour film. Some specimens do not lend themselves to this treatment and these have been illustrated by water-colour drawings.

The oak cynipids have been drawn to scale with the aid of a stereo-microscope, in addition a number of galls have been sectioned and treated in the same way to show the developing larva or pupa *in situ*.

Plant galls often exhibit a degree of variation and in some cases it has been possible to portray this in a short series. The remainder are all typical examples and as such we trust they will provide a valuable aid to identification.

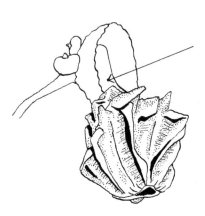

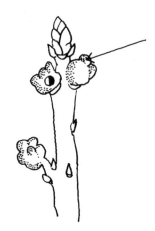

(a) Agamic gall of *Andricus quercus-calicis*, length 2 cm. Strand indicated connecting infested acorn with base of cup.

(b) Agamic galls of *Andricus corruptrix*, diameter 3–5 mm. Apical protuberances indicated.

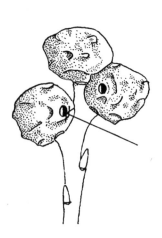

(c) Agamic galls of *Andricus lignicola*, each 10 × 8 mm. Escape hole of causer indicated.

(d) Bisexual gall of *Andricus quercus-ramuli*, diameter 2–3 cm, on staminate catkin.

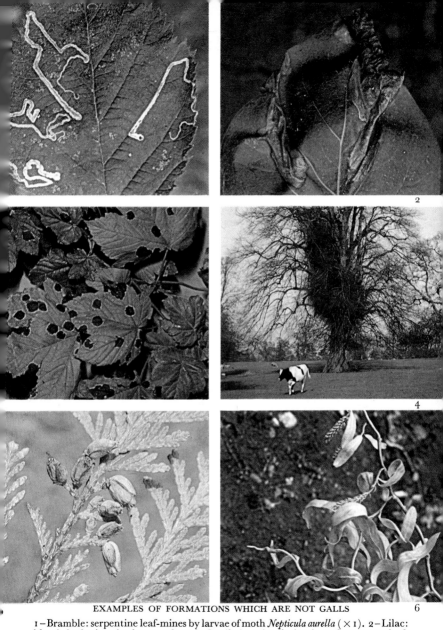

EXAMPLES OF FORMATIONS WHICH ARE NOT GALLS

1 – Bramble: serpentine leaf-mines by larvae of moth *Nepticula aurella* (×1). 2 – Lilac: blotch leaf-mines by larvae of moth *Gracilaria syringella* (×1). 3 – Sycamore: leaf-blotch by fungus *Rhytisma acerinum* (×¼). 4 – Lime: witches-broom induced by mechanical injury (×$\frac{1}{100}$). 5 – *Thuja occidentalis*: immature cones (×⅔). 6 – Pekin willow (*Salix matsudana tortuosa*): contortions due to unequal growth (×¼).

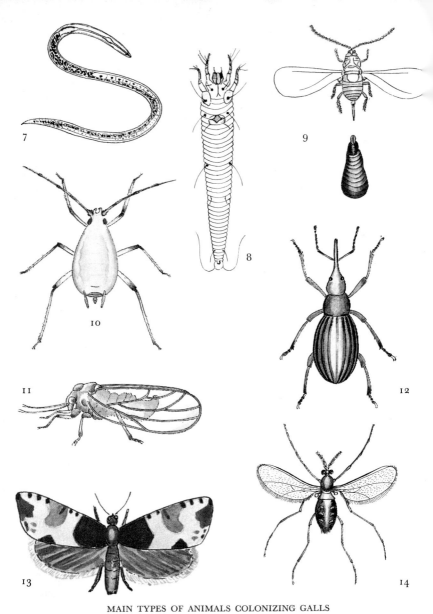

MAIN TYPES OF ANIMALS COLONIZING GALLS

7–Eelworm. 8–Eriophyid mite. 9–Coccids, *upper* ♂, *lower* ♀. 10–Aphid. 11–Psyllid =jumping plant louse. 12–Weevil. 13–Microlepidopteran. 14–Gall-midge.

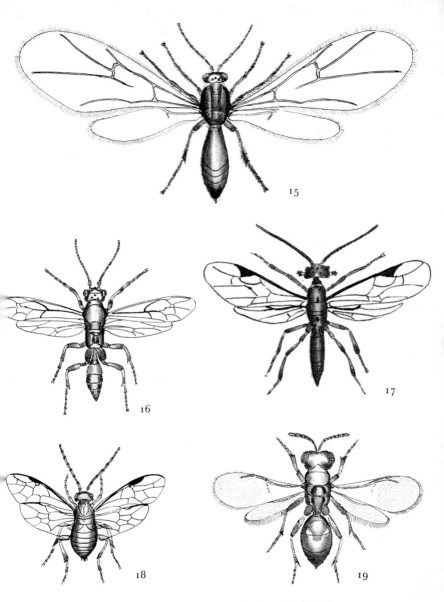

MAIN TYPES OF ANIMALS COLONIZING GALLS

15–Gall-wasp. 16–Ichneumon-fly. 17–Braconid=supplementary ichneumon-fly.
18–Sawfly. 19–Chalcid-wasp.
(Not to scale.)

20

21

22

GALLS OF DIPTERA ON FERNS

20–Bracken: pinnule margin rolled by gall-midge *Dasyneura filicina* (indicated).
21, 22–Male fern: rachis coiled by muscid *Chirosia parvicornis*. (All × 1.)

GALLED CONIFERS

23

24

25

26

27

Witches-broom fungus *Melampsorella caryophyllacearum* on silver fir: 23 – Initial stages (× 1); 24 – Old gall (× ⅓). Aphid pseudocone galls including *Adelges abietis* on spruce: 25 – Mature gall (× 1½); 26 – Old gall after emergence of causer (× ¾). Galls of eriophyid mites including *Eriophyes pini*: 27 – Cavities in old wood still colonized by mites (× ⅔).

30

GALLS OF FUNGUS *GYMNOSPORANGIUM*

28–Juniper: teleutospore stage (×⅔). 29–Hawthorn: aecidial stage of *G. clavariae-forme* (×1). 30–Mountain ash: aecidial stage of *G. juniperi* (×½). Indicated.

GALL-MIDGES ON CONIFER APICES

33

31 – Juniper: whooping gall *Oligotrophus juniperinus*. 32 – Yew: mature artichoke galls *Taxomyia taxi*. 33 – As 32: old artichoke galls after emergence of causer. (All × 1.)

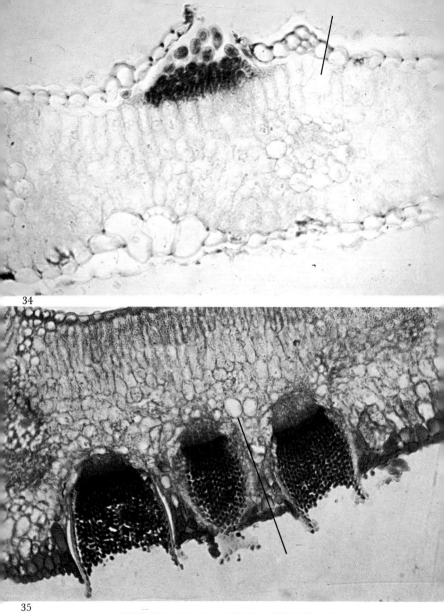

34

35

RUST *PUCCINIA GRAMINIS* ON BARBERRY LEAF

34–Spermogonium (section) on upper surface. 35–Aecidia (section) on lower surface. Preparations stained and enlarged cells of host indicated. (Both ×50.)

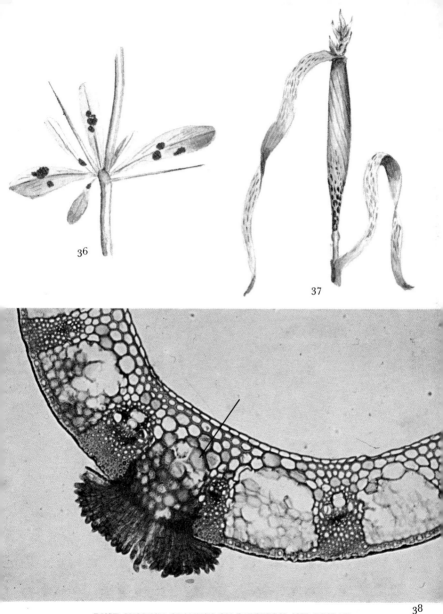

RUST *PUCCINIA GRAMINIS* ON BARBERRY AND WHEAT

36—Barberry: external appearance of spermogonial and aecidial galls (×1).
37—Wheat: external appearance of uredosori and teleutosori (×½). 38—As 37:
teleutospores in section (×50). Preparation stained and enlarged cells of host
indicated.

39

40

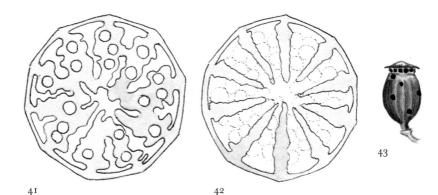

41

42

43

RUST AND SMUT GALLS

39–Common mallow: hollyhock rust *Puccinia malvacearum* on leaf (×2). 40–Wood anemone: crowfoot smut *Urocystis pompholygodes* on petiole (×1).

HYMENOPTERAN GALLS IN POPPY CAPSULES

41–Septa enlarged by *Aylax papaveris* (×4). 42–Ovules enlarged by *A. minor* (×4). 43–Galled capsule after emergence of causer (×1).

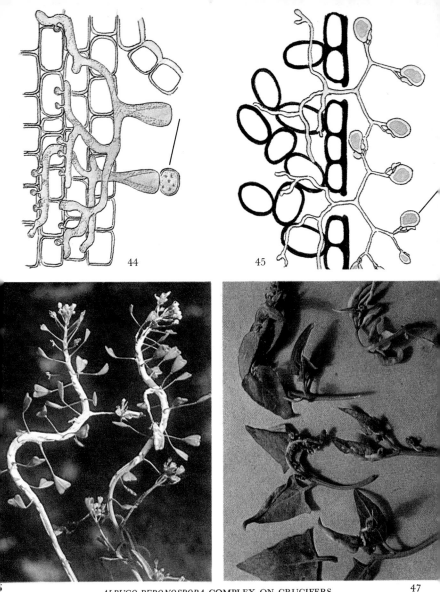

ALBUGO-PERONOSPORA COMPLEX ON CRUCIFERS

Sections through host showing conidia (indicated) and hyphae; preparations stained: 44–*Albugo*; 45–*Peronospora*. (Both × 50.) External appearance: 46– on shepherd's purse (×⅔).

APHID GALL ON ORACHE

47–Hastate orache: foliage rolled by *Hayhurstia atriplicis* (×½).

48   49

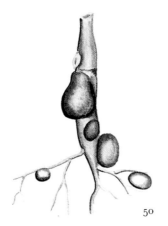   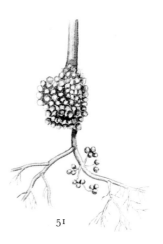

50   51

SUBTERRANEAN GALLS WITHOUT ALTERNATING GENERATIONS

48 – Swede: crown-gall *Agrobacterium tumefaciens* ($\times\frac{1}{4}$). 49 – Cabbage: club-root *Plasmodiophora brassicae* ($\times\frac{1}{2}$). 50 – Cabbage: turnip-and-cabbage gall-weevil *Ceuthorhynchus pleurostigma* ($\times\frac{1}{6}$). 51 – Alder: ? slime-fungus *Plasmodiophora alni* ($\times\frac{1}{4}$).

SUBTERRANEAN GALLS WITHOUT ALTERNATING GENERATIONS

52–Lupin: root-nodules of *Rhizobium beyerinckii* ($\times\frac{1}{3}$). 53–Clover: root-nodules of *Rhizobium radicicola*, indicated ($\times 1$). 54–Potato: black scab *Synchitrium endobioticum* ($\times\frac{1}{2}$). 55–Tomato: eelworm *Heterodera* sp. ($\times\frac{1}{4}$).

LEAF GALLS OF ERIOPHYID MITES ON LIME

56–Nail gall *E. tiliae typicus* ($\times \frac{1}{2}$). 57–*E. tiliae exilis* ($\times \frac{3}{4}$). 58–Roll gall *E. tetrastichus*, indicated ($\times \frac{1}{4}$). 59–*E. leiosoma* ($\times \frac{1}{3}$).

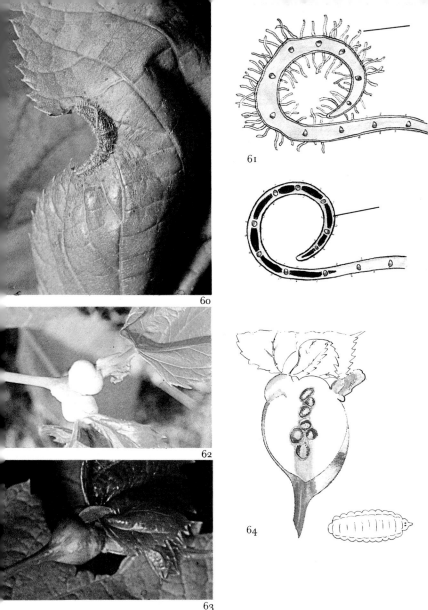

61

60

62

63

64

GALL-MIDGES ON LIME FOLIAGE

Roll galls of *Dasyneura* spp.: 60−*D. thomasiana* (×1); 61−Sections through *D. thoma-siana* (upper) and *D. tiliamvolvens* (lower) with contrasting features indicated (×5). Petiole gall of *Contarinia tiliarum*: 62−Immature (×1); 63−Mature (×1); 64−Section (×2½), with larval cavities and larvae.

65   66   67

LIME GALL
DIDYMOMYIA
SERIES

GALL-MIDGE *DIDYMOMYIA REAMURIANA* ON LIME LEAVES
65–Upper surface; 66–Lower surface: developing galls. 67–Mature galls.

GALL-MIDGE *DIDYMOMYIA REAMURIANA* ON LIME LEAVES

68–Mature galls. 69–Upper surface; 70–Lower surface: old galls with emergence hole indicated. (All ×1.) 71–'Escape capsule' ejected from ripe gall (×8).

72

73

LEAF GALLS OF ERIOPHYID MITES ON MAPLE

72−*E. macrochelus* ($\times \frac{1}{2}$). 73−*E. macrorhynchus cephalodes* ($\times \frac{2}{3}$).

LEAF GALLS OF ERIOPHYID MITES ON SYCAMORE

74—*E. megalonyx: left,* lower surface; *right,* upper surface ($\times \frac{1}{3}$). Forms of *E. macrorhynchus aceribus:* 75—Large, thin-walled, flaccid pustules, indicated ($\times \frac{1}{2}$); 76—Small, thick-walled, hard pustules, indicated ($\times \frac{1}{3}$).

77

78

79

LEAF-MINE GALL

77–Holly: leaves mined by agromyzid-fly *Phytomyza ilicis* (×½).

SHOOT APICES GALLED BY INSECTS

78–Box: cabbage gall of jumping plant louse *Psylla buxi*, comprising loosely packed leaves with some distorted on older growths, both indicated (×1). 79–Hedge mustard: more compact mass by gall-midge *Dasyneura sisymbrii* (×1).

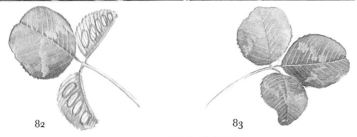

GALLS ON WHITE CLOVER

80 – Infected inflorescence: 4 stages in development of phyllanthous gall. 81 – Un-galled inflorescence: 5 stages in development. 82 – Leaflets galled by midge *Dasyneura trifolii*. 83 – Ungalled leaf. (All × 1.)

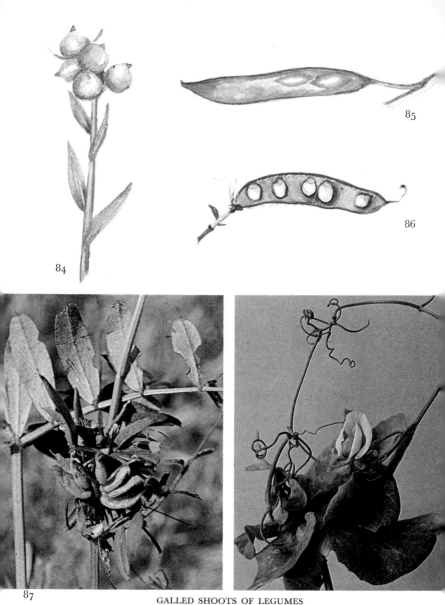

84   85   86   87

GALLED SHOOTS OF LEGUMES

84–Dyer's greenweed: midge *Jaapiella genisticola* on terminal leaves ($\times \frac{2}{3}$).
85–Broom: galls of midge *Asphondylia sarothamni* in pod ($\times 1$). 86–Broom: un-
infected pod ($\times 1$). 87–Common vetch: leaflets galled by midge *Contarinia loti*
($\times 1\frac{1}{2}$). Indicated. 88–Culinary pea: part of flowering shoot distorted by eelworm
Tylenchus devastatrix ($\times 1$).

INSECT GALLS ON *FILIPENDULA* AND *POTENTILLA*

89 – Meadowsweet: midge *Dasyneura ulmariae* on leaf. 90 – Creeping cinquefoil: gall-wasp *Xestophanes potentillae* on petiole. 91 – Common tormentil: gall-wasp *X. brevitarsis* on stem. (All × 1.)

92 **93**

94

OLD GALLS OF INSECTS IN BRAMBLE STEMS

92–Gall-midge *Lasioptera rubi* from interior of scrub (×1). 93–Gall-wasp *Diastrophus rubi* from perimeter of scrub (×1). 94–*D. rubi*: typical distortions (×½).

95

96

FOLD GALLS IN ROSE LEAFLETS

95–Gall-midge *Wachtiella rosarum*. Indicated. 96–Sawfly *Blennocampa pusilla* from below. (Both ×1.)

97

98

PEA GALLS ON ROSE LEAFLETS

97–Smooth pea gall *Diplolepis eglanteriae* in atypical position on upper surface.
98–Spiked pea gall *D. nervosus* in typical position on lower surface. (Both × 1½.)

99   100

101   102

ROSE BEDEGUAR *DIPLOLEPIS ROSAE*

99–Developing bedeguars, midsummer. 100–Full-grown bedeguar, late summer.
101–Bedeguar at onset of pupation phase, early winter. 102–Bedeguar after
emergence of causer, May. Note empty larval cells. (All ×1.)

103

104

105

GALLS ON *PRUNUS*

103—Blackthorn: leaves infested by gall-mite *Eriophyes similis* ($\times \frac{2}{3}$). 104—Black-thorn: fruit infested by bladder bullace fungus *Taphrina pruni* ($\times \frac{1}{2}$). 105—Black-thorn: uninfested fruits ($\times \frac{1}{2}$).

GALLS ON *PRUNUS*

106–Almond: peach-leaf curl fungus *Taphrina deformans* (×1). 107–Cherry: aphid
Myzus cerasi on terminal leaves (×1⅓).

108

109

1

GALLS ON HAWTHORN LEAVES

108–Mite *Eriophyes goniothorax typicus* on margins ($\times \frac{2}{3}$) indicated. Aphid *Dysaphis ranunculi* on blades: 109–Entire blade rolled into pouch ($\times 1$); 110–Multiple pouches in blade ($\times 1\frac{1}{2}$).

GALL-MIDGE *DASYNEURA CRATAEGI* ON HAWTHORN

111 – Single rosette ($\times \frac{2}{3}$). 112 – Appearance against sky ($\times \frac{1}{4}$).

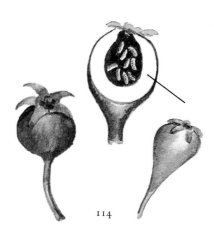

GALLS ON PEAR

113 – Pear-leaf blister of eriophyid mite *E. pyri* ($\times \frac{2}{3}$). 114 – Black pear of gall-midge *Lestodiplosis pyri*: *top*, opened fruit containing exceptional number of larvae (swollen receptacle indicated); *left*, external appearance of gall; *right*, normal fruit. (All $\times 1$.)

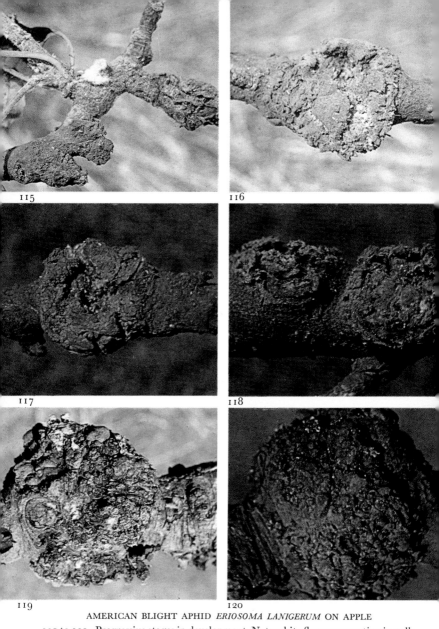

115 116

117 118

119 120

AMERICAN BLIGHT APHID *ERIOSOMA LANIGERUM* ON APPLE

115 to 120—Progressive stages in development. Note white floccose secretion in galls still occupied by causer. (All ×⅛.)

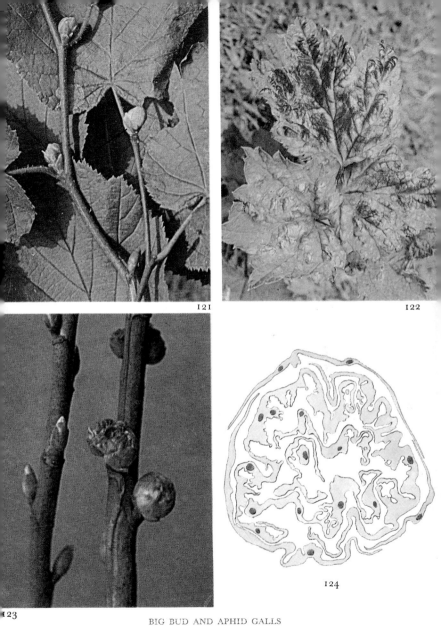

BIG BUD AND APHID GALLS

121–Hazel: bud gall (indicated) by mite *Eriophyes avellanae* ($\times\frac{1}{2}$). 122—Red currant: blister galls on foliage by aphid *Cryptomyzus ribis* ($\times\frac{1}{2}$). 123–Black currant: big bud by mite *Eriophyes ribis* ($\times 1$). Colonized stem *right*, uncolonized stem *left*. 124–Black currant: big bud gall in section ($\times 6$).

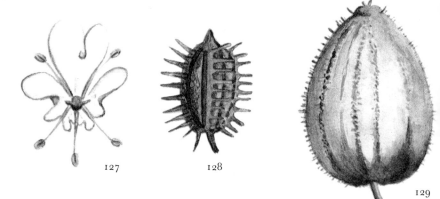

SHOOT GALLS ON DOGWOOD, IVY AND CARROT

125–Dogwood: gall-midge *Craneiobia corni* (×1). 126–'Parsley' ivy: eriophyid mite increasing leaf-edge folding (indicated); *left*, infested; *right*, uninfested (×1). Gall-midge *Kiefferia pimpinellae* on carrot inflorescence: 127–Single uninfested flower; 128–Fruit (cremocarp) from uninfested flower; 129–Gall from infested flower. (All ×7.)

INSECT GALLS ON PERSICARIA AND NETTLE LEAVES

Midge *Wachtiella persicariae* on persicaria: 130–Infested blades (×1); 131–Un-infested plants (×½). 132–Stinging nettle: leaf crinkle by psyllid (jumping plant louse) *Trioza urticae* (×½). Nettle gnat, *Dasyneura urticae*, on stinging nettle: 133–Infested blades (×½); 134–Infested leaf-axils (×1).

135

136

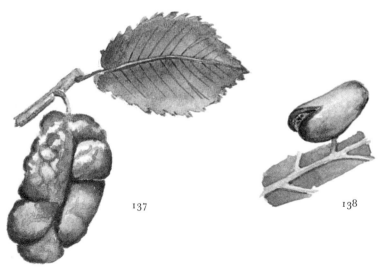

137

138

APHID GALLS ON ELM LEAVES

Roll gall of *Eriosoma ulmi* on wych elm: 135–Initial phase ($\times 1$); 136–Mature specimens ($\times \frac{1}{2}$). 137–Pouch gall of *Schizoneura lanuginosa* ($\times \frac{3}{4}$). 138–Fig gall of *Tetraneura ulmi* ($\times 2$).

GALLS ON WALNUT, HORNBEAM AND BIRCH LEAVES

Eriophyid mites: 139–Walnut: *E. tristriatus typicus* (×1), indicated; 140–Birch: *E. lionotus* (×2); 141–Hornbeam: *E. pulchellum* (×¾). Gall-midge: 142–Hornbeam: *Zygobia carpini*, lower surface *left*, upper surface *right* (×½), indicated.

COLONIZATION
OF ALDER
FOLIAGE

143

144

145

COLONIZATION OF ALDER FOLIAGE

Eriophyid mites: 143–*E. laevis inangulis*, upper surface; 144–*E. axillare*, upper surface; 145–As 144, lower surface.

146, 147

148

COLONIZATION OF ALDER FOLIAGE

146—*E. brevitarsus*, upper surface; 147—As 146, lower surface. (All ×1.) Gall-midge *Dasyneura alni*: 148—Roll galls, upper surface (×⅔). Swollen veins indicated.

149 150

151

BEECH LEAVES GALLED BY ERIOPHYID MITES

149–Filzgalls of *E. nervisequus* on lateral veins (indicated). 150–Roll galls of *E. stenopis typicus* (indicated). 151–Pouch galls of *E. macrorhynchus ferruginus* between major veins. (All × 1.)

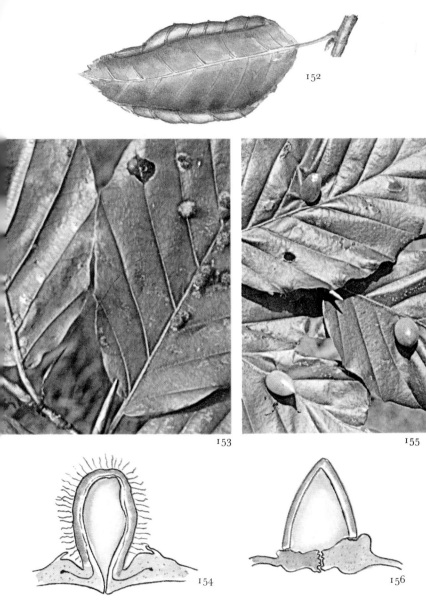

BEECH LEAVES GALLED BY INSECTS

152–Aphid *Phyllaphis fagi* (× ⅔). 153–Gall-midge *Hartigiola annulipes*: *left*, lower surface; *right*, upper surface (× 1). 154–As 153: vertical section through gall (× 6). 155–Gall-midge *Mikiola fagi*, upper surface (× 1). 156–As 155: vertical section through gall (× 3).

157

158

159

INSECTS OTHER THAN CYNIPIDS ON OAK

157–Pit-gall coccid *Asteriolecanium variolosum*: old galls (indicated). 158–Gall-midge *Macrodiplosis dryobia* on lower surface of leaf. 159–Gall-midge *M. volvens* on upper surface of leaf. (All ×1.)

160   161   162

163

OAK APPLE CYNIPID *BIORHIZA PALLIDA*

A–Bisexual generation: colour phases. 160–Galls near maturity. 161–Mature gall
(remains of scale-leaves of former terminal bud indicated). 162–Old galls beginning to
shrivel. (All ×½.) B–Agamic generation. 163–Mature root galls (×1½).

164

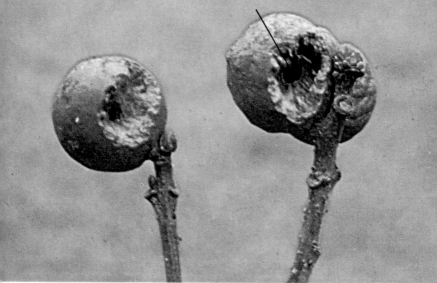

165

OAK MARBLE CYNIPID *ANDRICUS KOLLARI*

A–Agamic generation. 164–Developing gall (×1). 165–Two galls (*right*, coalesced) from which causer has been extracted by bird predator (×2). Larval cell indicated.

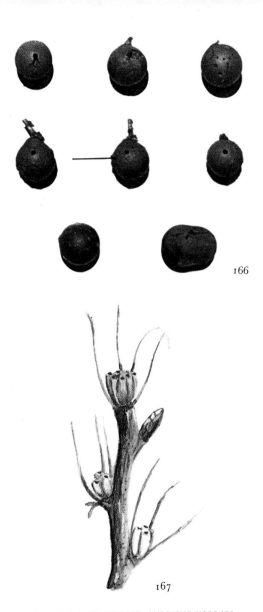

166

167

OAK MARBLE CYNIPID *ANDRICUS KOLLARI*

A–Agamic generation (*cont.*). Old galls. 166–*Top:* single escape-hole of causer and smaller holes of inquilines, etc. *Middle:* emerged galls colonized by fungus *Phoma gallorum* (indicated). *Bottom:* failures–*left,* through premature death of occupant; *right,*? through vegetative abnormalities. (All ×½.) B–Bisexual generation. 167–Turkey oak: 'ant-pupa' galls of *Andricus circulans* (×1).

168

OAK CYNIPID *ANDRICUS FECUNDATOR*

A–Agamic generation. 168–Group of artichoke galls (×1). B–Bisexual generation.
169–Hairy catkin galls on male inflorescence (×6).

169

170

171

OAK CYNIPID *ANDRICUS CURVATOR*

A–Agamic generation. 170–Collared-bud gall: *left*, position (×1); *right*, appearance at maturity (×6), with protrusion of inner core indicated. B–Bisexual generation. 171–Curved-leaf gall (× 1½).

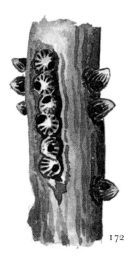

OAK CYNIPID *ANDRICUS TESTACEIPES*

172–Red barnacle galls of agamic generation (×1). 173–Leaf-vein galls of bisexual generation (×1).

OAK CYNIPID *ANDRICUS INFLATOR*

174–Twig galls of bisexual generation after emergence of causer (×1). 175–Globular gall of agamic generation (×2).

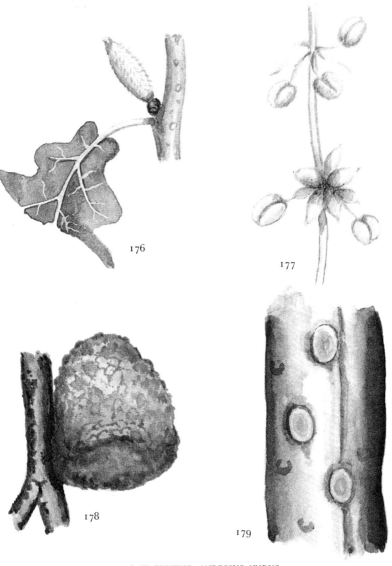

OAK CYNIPID *ANDRICUS NUDUS*

176–Malpighi's gall of agamic generation (×5). 177–Bald-seed galls of bisexual generation (×5).

OAK CYNIPID *ANDRICUS QUERCUS-RADICIS*

178–Truffle gall of agamic generation (×1). 179–Knot galls of bisexual generation exposed by removal of bark (×5).

180

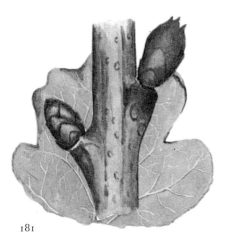

181

OAK CYNIPID *CYNIPS DIVISA*

A–Agamic generation. 180–Red-pea galls in typical position on leaf-veins and midrib ($\times \frac{1}{2}$). B–Bisexual generation. 181–Red-wart gall compared with uncolonized bud ($\times 5$).

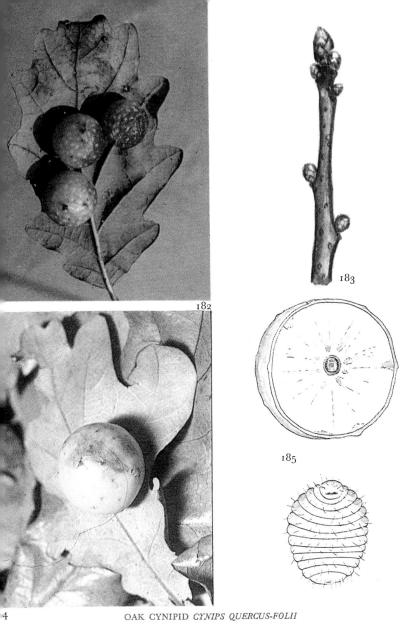

84

OAK CYNIPID *CYNIPS QUERCUS-FOLII*

182–Cherry galls of agamic generation developing on underside of leaf-veins ($\times 1$).
183–Violet-egg galls of bisexual generation contrasted with uncolonized buds ($\times 1$).
184–Single cherry gall at maturity ($\times 1\frac{1}{8}$). 185–Cherry gall in section showing median larval chamber and single occupant ($\times 1\frac{3}{4}$).

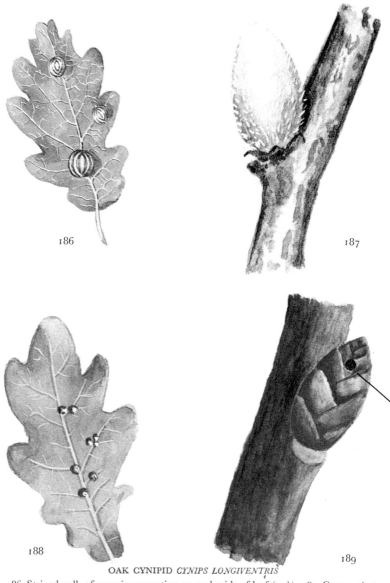

186   187

188   189

OAK CYNIPID *CYNIPS LONGIVENTRIS*

186–Striped galls of agamic generation on underside of leaf ($\times \frac{1}{2}$). 187–Green velvet bud gall of bisexual generation ($\times 12$).

OAK CYNIPID *ANDRICUS OSTREUS*

188–Oyster gall of agamic generation in typical position on underside of leaf ($\times \frac{2}{3}$).
189–April-bud gall of bisexual generation ($\times 5$). Escape aperture indicated.

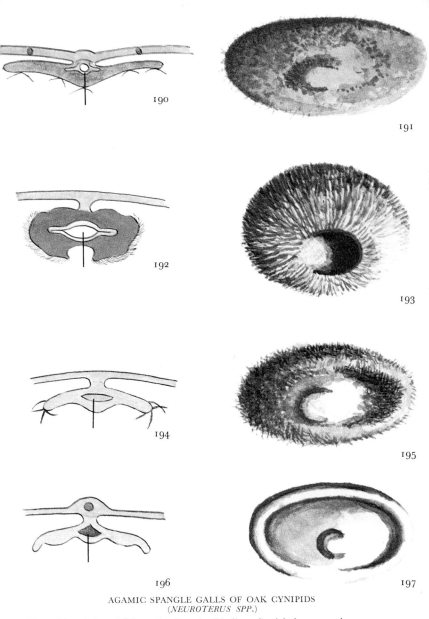

AGAMIC SPANGLE GALLS OF OAK CYNIPIDS
(*NEUROTERUS SPP.*)

Viewed from below: *left*, in section (larval cell indicated); *right*, in perspective. 190, 191–
Common spangle *N. quercus-baccarum*. 192, 193–Silk-button spangle *N. numismalis*.
194, 195–Cupped spangle *N. tricolor*. 196, 197–Smooth spangle *N. albipes*. (Scale:
sections × 8, entire galls × 10.)

198

199

200

OAK CYNIPID *NEUROTERUS QUERCUS-BACCARUM*

A–Agamic generation. 198–Young common spangle galls developing on underside of leaf ($\times 1\frac{1}{2}$). Central elevation indicated. B–Bisexual generation. 199–Maturing currant galls on male catkins. 200–Currant galls in less familiar position on young foliage. (Both $\times 1$.)

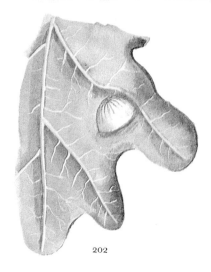

201

202

OAK CYNIPID *NEUROTERUS NUMISMALIS*

201–Silk-button spangle galls of agamic generation ($\times \frac{2}{3}$). 202–Blister gall of bi-sexual generation ($\times 3$).

204

203

OAK CYNIPID *NEUROTERUS TRICOLOR*

203–Cupped spangle galls (indicated) of agamic generation. 204–Hairy-pea galls of bisexual generation. (Both $\times 1$.)

205

206

207

OAK CYNIPID *NEUROTERUS ALBIPES*

A–Agamic generation. 205–Smooth spangle galls developing in typical position on underside of leaf ($\times 1\frac{1}{2}$). B–Bisexual generation. 206–Schenck's gall (indicated) in typical position within recessed leaf-margin ($\times 1$). 207–Schenck's galls (*left*, early phase; *right*, late phase) in atypical position on outer curve of margin ($\times 2$).

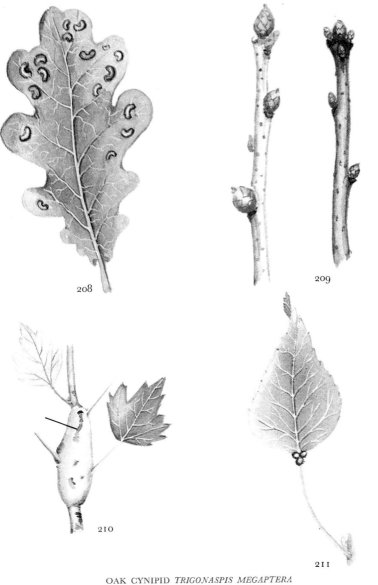

OAK CYNIPID *TRIGONASPIS MEGAPTERA*

208–Kidney galls of agamic generation. 209–Pink-bud galls of bisexual generation.
(Both × 1.)

COLONIZATION OF POPLARS

210–White poplar: moth *Gypsonoma aceriana* in stem (× 1). Excreta indicated.
211–Black Italian poplar: leaf-glands galled by eriophyid mite *E. diversipunctatus*
(× ½).

GALL-MIDGES ON ASPEN FOLIAGE

212—Galls of *Harmandia globuli* on midrib and major veins ($\times \frac{2}{3}$). 213—Leaf cluster infested by ripe galls of *Syndiplosis petioli* ($\times \frac{1}{3}$). 214—Ditto: detached leaves showing appearance of old galls ($\times \frac{1}{2}$).

FOLIAGE OF LOMBARDY POPLAR GALLED BY APHIDS
(*PEMPHIGUS* AND *THECABIUS*)

215–Purse gall *P. bursarius* on petiole: note 'pouting' form of escape aperture ($\times 1\frac{1}{2}$).
216–Fundatrix gall of *P. lysimachiae* ($\times 1\frac{1}{2}$). 217–First-generation galls of *Thecabius affinis* ($\times \frac{2}{3}$). 218–Spiral gall on petiole: stages in development following initial attack (*top left*) by fundatrix ($\times \frac{2}{3}$).

219   220

221

FUNGUS *ASCOMYCES AUREUS* ON POPLAR LEAVES

219, 220–White poplar: *left*, upper surface; *right*, lower surface (×1). 221–
Lombardy poplar: *top*, upper surface; *bottom*, lower surface (×⅔). Note occasional
'inverted' pouches.

222

223

224

225

GALLS MAINLY ON GOAT WILLOW

222—Gall-midge *Iteomyia capreae* on leaf ($\times \frac{2}{3}$). 223—Beetle *Saperda populnea* in stem ($\times \frac{2}{3}$). 224—Gall-midge *Rhabdophaga heterobia* on male catkin ($\times 1\frac{1}{2}$). 225—Eriophyid mite *E. tetanothorax* on foliage ($\times \frac{1}{2}$).

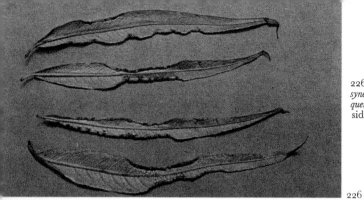

226–Gall-midge *I
syneura marginemt
quens*, from und
side (×½).

226

227–Out-pocketin
of margin by eri
phyid mite *E. ma
ginatus*: *left*, upp
surface; *right*, low
surface (×⅔).

227

228–Unilateral cur
vatures induced b
eriophyids (×½).

228

LEAF-MARGIN GALLS ON WILLOW

229

230

231

232

SAWFLIES *PONTANIA* SPP. ON WILLOW LEAVES

Bean gall sawfly *P. proxima*: 229–Undersides of galls in greenish/yellow phase; 230–Galls in red/red phase: *left*, upper surface; *right*, lower surface. (Both $\times\frac{1}{2}$.) 231–*P. viminalis* near underside of midrib ($\times 1$). 232–*P. vesicator* on underside between lateral veins ($\times\frac{1}{2}$).

233

234

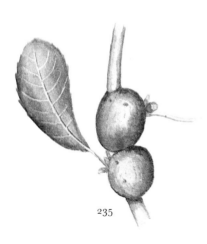

235

236

COLONIZATION OF WILLOWS BY DIPTERA

Camellia gall of gall-midge *Rhabdophaga rosaria*: 233–Rosette on goat willow ($\times$1);
234–'Double gall' on white willow ($\times$1$\frac{1}{3}$); note leaf-edge colonization by *Eriophyes marginatus* (indicated). Stem galls: 235–Gall-midge *Rhabdophaga salicis* ($\times$1);
236–Agromyzid-fly *Agromyza schineri* ($\times$$\frac{1}{2}$).

BASIDIOMYCETE FUNGI ON
WHORTLEBERRY

237–*Calyptospora goeppertiana* (*left*)
compared with ungalled shoot
($\times \frac{1}{2}$). 238–*Exobasidium vaccinii*
($\times \frac{2}{3}$).

237

238

239

240

FASCIATION OF *FORSYTHIA*

239–Shoot fasciated by *Corynebacterium fascians*. 240–Clustered-bud galls associated
with same. (Both $\times \frac{1}{2}$.)

241

242

243

FASCIATION: FOUR EXAMPLES

241–Dogwood: spatulate main axis with vertical curvature ($\times\frac{1}{6}$). 242–Ribwort plantain: strap-like development of scape with fasciated inflorescence ($\times\frac{1}{2}$). 243–*Euphorbia wulfenii*: spatulate main axis, undersized foliage and some normal inflorescences ($\times\frac{1}{4}$). 244–Holly: spatulate axis with forking and partial clockwise rotation, loss of chlorophyll and accumulation of anthocyanin *red* and β carotin *yellow* ($\times\frac{1}{4}$).

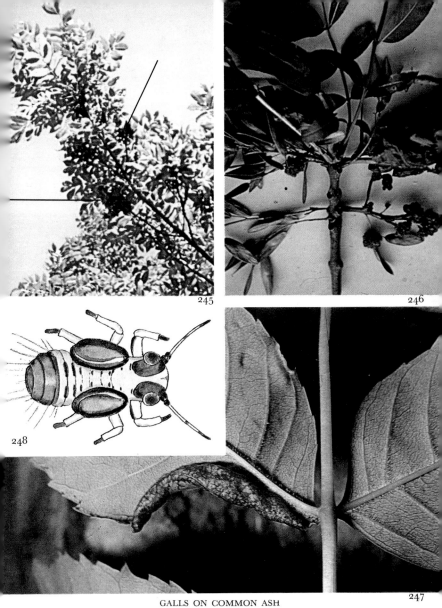

245 246

248

247

GALLS ON COMMON ASH

Inflorescence galls of eriophyid mite, *E. fraxinivorus*: 245—Appearance among foliage from ground ($\times \frac{1}{20}$), indicated; 246—Partly galled flower-clusters ($\times \frac{1}{2}$). Leaflet edge rolled by jumping plant louse *Psyllopsis fraxini*: 247—Mature gall on underside of leaflet ($\times 3$); 248—Nymphal causer removed from gall ($\times 18$).

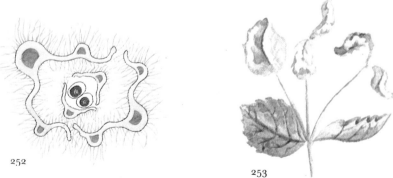

GALL-MIDGE *DASYNEURA FRAXINI* ON ASH LEAFLETS

249 – Lower surface. 250 – Upper surface: longitudinal furrow indicated. (Both ×⅓.)

COLONIZATION OF SPEEDWELL

251 – Gall-midge *Jaapiella veronicae* on terminal leaves (×1⅓). 252 – As 251, gall in section (×4). 253 – Eriophyid mite *E. anceps* on terminal leaves (×1).

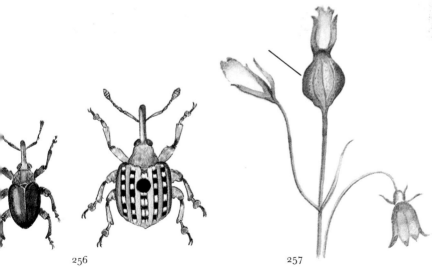

254   255

256   257

FLOWER GALLS OF WEEVILS

254–Figwort: *Gymnetron* sp. on shoots, indicated ($\times \frac{1}{3}$). 255–Figwort: detached flowers; *upper*, ungalled; *lower*, galled by *Gymnetron* ($\times 2$). 256–Weevils colonizing figwort: *left*, gall-causer *Gymnetron*; *right*, non-causer *Cionus* ($\times 6$). 257–Hairbell: infestation by *Miarus campanulae* indicated ($\times 1$).

258

259

ERIOPHYID MITE *E. THOMASI* ON THYME

258–General appearance of infested plants in sward ($\times \frac{1}{3}$). 259–Individual galled inflorescences ($\times 1\frac{1}{2}$).

260

261

INSECT GALLS ON GROUND IVY

260 – Lighthouse galls of dipteron *Dasyneura glechomae* (× 1). 261 – Galls of hymenopteran *Liposthenus latreillei* (× 1½).

263

264

ERIOPHYID MITE *E. AJUGAE* ON BUGLE

262–Uninfested inflorescences (× ½). 263–Infested inflorescence (× ¾).

EELWORM *ANGUILLULINA* ON PLANTAIN

264–*Upper*, numerous small galls on infested leaf; *lower*, uninfested leaf (× 1).

265

267

266

MOTH *TORTRIX PALEANA* ON PLANTAIN

265 – Effects on fruiting spikes: *left*, uninfested spike with high seed-yield; *rest*, malformed spikes with low seed-yield (× 1). Extruded pupa indicated.

GALL-MIDGE *GEOCRYPTA GALII* ON BEDSTRAW

266 – Cove-ring galls (× 2) with escape pore indicated. 267 – Gall in section (× 5) showing chambers and larvae.

268

269

ERIOPHYID MITES ON GOOSEGRASS AND WAYFARING-TREE

268–Goosegrass: leaf-roll gall (indicated) of *E. galii* (×1). 269–Wayfaring tree: pouch-gall of *E. viburni* (×⅔). Infestation mainly as two bands on either side of midrib (*left*), and as single band on one side of midrib (*right*) – see text.

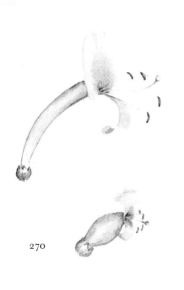

270

271

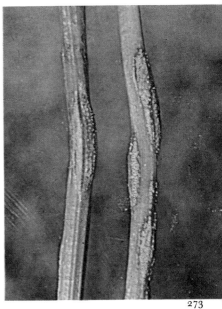

272

273

INFESTED HONEYSUCKLE, SCABIOUS AND GROUNDSEL

270–Honeysuckle: *upper*, normal flower; *lower*, flower galled by aphid *Hyadaphis foeniculi* (×2). 271–Scabious: eriophyid mite *E. squalidus*, on inflorescence (×1). 272–Groundsel: distortions in shoot by rust *Puccinia terrieriana* (×⅓). 273–As 272: tumefactions on stems (×2).

274 275

276

277

INFESTED COMPOSITES

274–Groundsel: inflorescences colonized by gall-midge *Contarinia jacobaeae* (indicated). 275–Groundsel: ungalled inflorescences. (Both ×1.) 276–Yarrow: leaf-rachis colonized by eelworm *Anguillulina millefolii* (×1). 277–Yarrow: axillary buds colonized by gall-midge *Rhopalomyia millefolii* (×⅔).

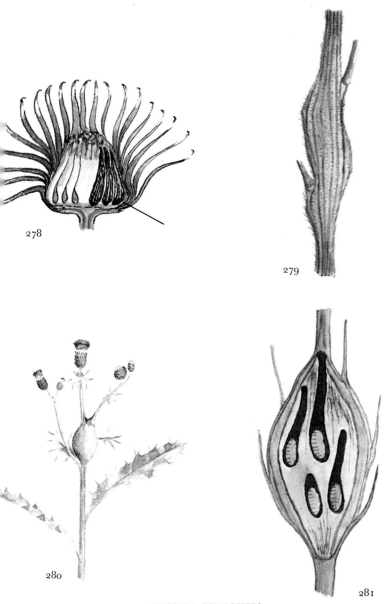

INFESTED COMPOSITES

278–Burdock: inflorescence (section) colonized by fruit-fly *Tephritis bardanae* (×2). Galls confined to right side (indicated). 279–Knapweed: gall-wasp *Isocolus scabiosae* in stem (×1). 280–Creeping thistle: fruit-fly *Euribia cardui* in stem (×⅓). 281–As 280: section through gall (×2).

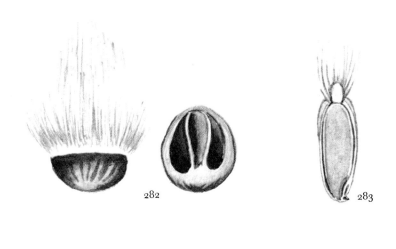

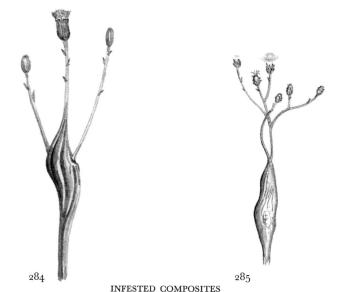

INFESTED COMPOSITES

282–Knapweed: fruit-fly *Euribia solstitialis* in seed; *left*, gall; *right*, larval chamber in gall (×2). 283–As 282: normal seed (×2). 284–Cat's ear: gall-wasp *Phanacis hypochaeridis* in shoot (×1). 285–Hawkweed: gall-wasp *Aulacidea hieracii* in shoot (×⅔).

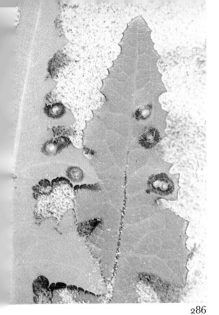

287

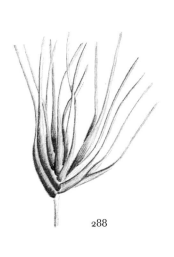

288

289

INFESTED COMPOSITES AND MONOCOTS

286 – Sow-thistle: foliage colonized by gall-midge *Cystiphora sonchi* (×¾). 287 – Wood blue-grass: gall-midge *Poamyia poae* in stem (×3). 288 – Rush: tassel gall of psyllid *Livia juncorum*. 289 – As 288: normal inflorescence. (Both ×½.)

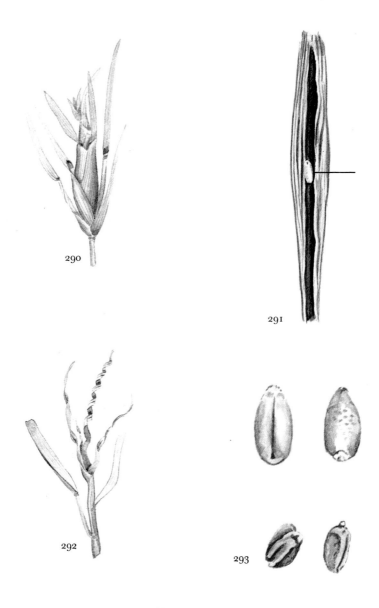

INFESTED GRASSES

290–Common reed: gall of chloropid *Lipara lucens* ($\times\frac{1}{2}$). 291–As 290: section through larval chamber ($\times$1). Causer indicated. 292–Couch-grass: infestation by chloropid *Chlorops taeniopus* ($\times\frac{1}{2}$). 293–Wheat: *upper*, normal grain; *lower*, young galls of eelworm *Tylenchus tritici*, developing in ovaries ($\times$3).

REPRESENTATIVE BRITISH GALLS

Commoner examples of the main types of gall arranged in the systematic order of their host plants after Clapham, Tutin and Warburg's *Flora of the British Isles* (1962).

In each case the plants named are those which the particular causer seems to colonize most frequently.

The bold figures in the outside margins indicate reference numbers to colour plates.

POLYPODIACEAE, Polypody family

Pteridium

Bracken (*P. aquilinum*) Pinnule galled by dipteron, gall-midge **Dasyneura filicina** (= *Perrisia filicina, Cecidomyia filicina, C. pteridis*).

'Little black pudding.' The gall originates from the downward rolling and slight thickening of one edge only of the pinnule, although opposite edges may be separately infested. Its typical form is that of a smooth, torpedo-shaped roll, slightly twisted in the long axis, rarely exceeding 0·5 cm in length, and looking something like a distorted indusium (which, in bracken, is continuous with the underside edge of the pinnule). It grows between June and August. As it matures, the colour darkens from yellowish green, through streaky russet, to brown and glossy black, by which time it suggests a tiny slug. Each gall contains a single larva which enters the soil to pupate, over-winters here, and the imago appears in the following spring. The causer is difficult to rear.

From above, its presence may be indicated by the slight distortion of the pinna and discoloration, the affected part generally turning yellow in the early stages. In practice, however, it is likely to be overlooked unless the pinnae are turned back and examined from the underside, or the observer lies on the ground beneath the overhanging fronds and inspects them by transmitted light.

Locally distributed. The parasite seems to be absent from some large tracts of country where bracken itself is abundant.

A mite, *Eriophyes pteridis*, causes a somewhat similar roll gall on bracken. A basic distinction between them is that the mite gall is hairy, whereas that of the insect is glabrous.

Dryopteris

Male Fern (*D. filix-mas*) Prickly Buckler Fern (*D. spinulosa*)

Frond galled by dipteron, muscid **Chirosia parvicornis.**

Widespread, particularly in the south

and west. Larvae develop from ova inserted in the frond and mine into the chlorophyllous tissue, causing the rachis to coil and the pinnae to become entwined. The general impression is that of a frond tied in a knot. Some of the pinnae enclosed in the loop quickly wither and turn brown or black. Distortion involves localized proliferation as well as atrophy of cells. Specimens develop from early summer and remain until the fronds collapse after frost.

Since the agent is one of a genus of tiny, grey flies, the naturalist may be puzzled by the absence of an obvious cause for what is generally a rather striking appearance. Probably the best way to find the fly is to rear it from material collected in late summer and kept over soil in a jar.

PINACEAE, Pine family
Abies

Silver Fir (*A. alba*)

Branch galled by fungus, basidiomycete **Melampsorella caryophyllacearum** (= *Aecidium elatinum, Peridermium elatinum*).

23-4

A 'witches-broom' gall of remarkable form. It becomes a sphere of variable size on a horizontal branch, with twigs arising more or less vertically, and in clusters, from the upper part. The causer is the aecidial generation of the fungus. Its hyphae penetrate into buds arising in the galled area, with the result that the needles developing from these buds become stunted, swollen, soft and pale. The aecidia of the fungus grow on these in June–July, and its spermogonia may appear as orange spots on the surface of the gall. Affected needles fall off when about a year old.

The uredospore and teleutospore generation develops in such members

of the family Caryophyllaceae as the chickweeds *Cerastium* and *Stellaria*.

Picea

Norway Spruce (*P. abies*)
Sitka Spruce (*P. sitchensis*)

Bases of leaves galled by homopteran, aphid **Adelges abietis** (= *A. gallarumabietis, Chermes abietis, Sacchiphantes abietis*).

'Pseudocone gall.' In spring (April) aphids newly hatched from over-wintered eggs feed at the bases of the growing needles: the punctures they make are followed by swelling of the bases, which eventually coalesce to form cone-like structures (pseudocones). At first yellowish green, the galls pass through pink to reddish brown. Length, about 1·5–2·0 cm.

A single pseudocone may contain over 100 cavities enclosing growing wingless aphids. The pseudocones mature in June–July when openings develop through which the insects crawl out on to the needles. Here they moult, develop wings and fly to other conifers, such as larch (*Larix*), pine (*Pinus*) and silver fir (*Abies alba*). Although several generations of aphids are raised on these secondary hosts, no galls are formed. In July of the following year, other winged individuals appear which return to the spruce and breed there, thus completing the life-cycle.

A peculiar gall which is frequently seen on Christmas trees.

Similar galls are produced by other aphids: on Sitka spruce by *Gilletteela cooleyi*, some generations of which migrate to Douglas fir (*Pseudotsuga taxifolia*); and on spruce by *Cnaphalodes* sp., which is heteroecious with larch.

Pinus

Scots Pine (*Pinus sylvestris*)
Twig galled by acarine, gall-mite
7 **Eriophyes pini.**

Oval swellings of variable size and the same general colour as the adjacent tissues sometimes affect the young twigs. The causer is a mite which, in two respects, is remarkable:

1. It lives communally in the intercellular spaces of the host instead of occupying a single, large cavity;

2. Although colonization is initiated in the new season's growth, while the tissues are still soft, the mites continue to breed in the same gall for several years after it has become woody, and the third-year needles have fallen. Locally common.

CUPRESSACEAE, Cypress family
Juniperus

Juniper (*J. communis*)
Stem galled by fungi, basidiomycetes
30 **Gymnosporangium** spp.

The teleutospore stage of several rust fungi of the genus *Gymnosporangium* causes a distortion of the stem of juniper, which begins as a unilateral swelling of the cortex and develops slowly, often over a period of years, eventually involving all sides and reaching the conducting tissues. Spatulate structures arise which project from the gall and consist of teleutospores embedded in mucilage. The dimensions of all such galls are very variable.

After release, those teleutospores which, by such agencies as wind or insects, happen to reach the damp young foliage of a suitable host, germinate here and develop into a second generation of the fungus, the aecidium stage. This also induces galls and can be particularly destructive to its host.

Three examples of rusts which behave in this way are the following.

Gymnosporangium juniperi. The aecidium generation develops from July to October on the leaflets of mountain ash (*Sorbus aucuparia*), and occasionally on the foliage of apple (*Malus sylvestris*). Visible signs of infestation include localized thickenings of the blade, each about 0·5 cm in diameter, reddish on the upper surface and greenish yellow or orange below, with spike-like filaments projecting from the lower surface composed of specialized hyphae forming the aecidial stage. These hyphae are homologous with the cluster-cups of some of the other rusts and release the aecidiospores which undergo development on juniper. The juniper gall is active in May and June, but the fungus can survive from year to year on this host.

G. sabinae. The aecidia cause thickened, reddish yellow spots, the 'pear-leaf cluster-cups', on the foliage of pear (*Pyrus communis*). Although most frequent on the leaves, they also occur on the fruit and young stems. This generation is often very harmful to pear trees, causing the leaves to fall prematurely so that the development of the crop and the hardening of the new wood are inhibited.

G. clavariaeforme (= *Raestelia lacerata*). The aecidia induce cluster-cups on hawthorn (*Crataegus monogyna*). These galls are abundant in some districts on young shoots in hedges, where they occur as swellings about 2·0 cm long in the softer parts of the twigs, and generally involve some leaves which swell and quickly decay. The colour is orange, russet or chocolate brown.

Chemical control of none of these rusts is easy, and the surest method of preventing infection is to remove and burn the infested branches of the juniper bushes in the vicinity.

Juniper
Apex of shoot galled by dipteron, gall-midge **Oligotrophus juniper-**
31 **inus.**

'Juniper berry' or 'whooping gall'. One of the English names is misleading, as it is not particularly fruit-like in appearance. It somewhat resembles the artichoke gall on yew caused by the midge *Taxomyia taxi* (Pl. 32, 33) since it consists of a cluster of needles at the tip of a shoot enclosing a single larva. The length is about 1·0 cm.

The gall has been used medicinally in the treatment of whooping-cough.

TAXACEAE, Yew family
Taxus

Yew (*T. baccata*)
Apex of shoot galled by dipteron, gall-
32-3 midge **Taxomyia** (= *Cecidomyia*) **taxi.**

'Artichoke gall of yew.' Elongation of the growing region is arrested, the tip swells, and of the 60–80 terminal leaves clustered to form a single gall, the outer ones are dark green and the inner nearly white. Long axis, 1·5–2·0 cm.

The galls mature in May–June while still retaining their compact shape. Each encloses a single larva which pupates inside the gall, the imago emerging a month later. Subsequently the leaves turn brown; or diverge from the stem axis, become reflexed and stay green. Old galls remain on the plant for a year or more.

A widespread and easily recognized species, which is frequently abundant every season on the same trees, young and old alike.

RANUNCULACEAE, Buttercup family
Anemone

Wood Anemone (*A. nemorosa*)
Ranunculus

Creeping Buttercup (*R. repens*)
Petiole and leaf-blade galled by fungus, smut **Urocystis** (= *Polycystis*) **pom-**
pholygodes. 4

'Crowfoot-smut.' Considerable swelling and distortion of the affected parts lead to the formation of galls of very variable size. The leaf-blade may become 'pinched-off' from the petiole and fall, after which the petiole often assumes a spiral form. From April to late summer, the colours of the outer tissues change from greenish yellow to red and purple. The epidermis splits in autumn, and a powdery mass of black, sporogenous tissue becomes exposed.

The species is often abundant particularly in wet situations.

BERBERIDACEAE, Barberry family
Berberis

Barberry (*B. vulgaris*)
Leaf galled by aecidial generation of fungus, basidiomycete **Puccinia gra-**
minis. 34

'Black rust of wheat.' The life-cycle is complicated and is represented schematically in Fig. 3. It involves the colonization of two hosts, barberry and wheat (*Triticum aestivum* or *T. turgidum*), in regular alternation.

The leaves of barberry become infested in spring and bear galls of two kinds: dots (*spermogonia*) on the upper surface, which are really flask-shaped in section and which change from yellow to brown; and orange-coloured pustules (cluster-cups or *aecidia*) on the lower surface. Complicated changes in the spermogonia give rise to the cluster-cups and these, in turn, bud off *aecidiospores* which are readily dispersed by wind.

Should an aecidiospore come to rest on a leaf of wheat, it germinates and produces a slender tube (hypha) which enters the leaf through a stoma. Here an extensive mycelium develops which induces swelling in the tissues and eventually ruptures the epidermis in brown lines (*uredosori*). From these, *uredospores* are released which become airborne and are capable of rapidly infesting other wheat plants through the stomata. Later in the summer, the uredosori turn black and give rise to *teleutospores*. Each of these is two-celled: it is essentially a resting-stage capable of withstanding winter conditions, and normally germinates only after lying in the stubble until spring. When it does so, it releases 8 *basidiospores* (4 from each cell), which are carried in air-currents: if one of these alights on a young leaf of barberry, it produces a hypha capable of directly piercing the epidermis of the host and setting up the mycelium within the leaf which causes the spermogonia and cluster-cups.

The galls are small, and their full beauty is revealed only in section.

A pest which is unevenly distributed and tends to be persistent where it does occur. The regular alternation between the two hosts, barberry and wheat, is essential if the rust is to maintain itself, so that one method of control is to break the life-cycle by destroying barberry bushes in the vicinity of wheatfields.

39 'Hollyhock rust' (*Puccinia malvacearum*) Pl. 39 forms an interesting contrast. This rust is comparatively unspecialized and, instead of being restricted to a single herbaceous and single woody host, is capable of infesting many plants belonging to the Malvaceae (hollyhock family), being particularly frequent on common mallow (*Malva sylvestris*) and other species of *Malva*, *Lavatera* (tree mallows), *Althaea* (hollyhocks), and members of the genera *Abutilon* and *Sidalcea*. Infestation generally shows as little pustulate galls on the long petiole or the underside of the leaf-blade or veins. Although only very small, the host's proliferations may be sufficiently dense to bring about localized distortion of the affected part.

Groups scattered on the leaf-blade of common mallow tend to be thickest towards the margins. Here each gall first shows as a shiny, lenticular spot, about 0·1 cm in diameter, which is paler than the rest of the leaf and which becomes hemispherical and matt with the development of sporogenous tissue, darkening with age to orange and finally to red-brown. The colouring may be uniform or there may be a yellowish areola surrounding the darker centre. A few pustules often erupt through the upper epidermis: the positions of the rest are indicated on this surface by shallow, pale depressions. Affected areas of the petiole or a vein are more distinctly swollen, when they are the same colour as the leaf-blade pustules but somewhat larger.

Only the teleutospore stage of hollyhock rust is known and there is no alternation between two hosts. The teleutospores are capable of germinating immediately they reach maturity and generally do so *in situ* on the host, the two cells of each producing four basidiospores apiece which can immediately infest any of the possible hosts. Some teleutospores lie dormant during the winter before releasing basidiospores.

The history of hollyhock rust has been interesting: first recorded from Chile in 1852, it appeared in Spain in 1869 and in England in 1873. Its distribution is now world-wide.

PAPAVERACEAE, Poppy family
Papaver

> Field Poppy (*P. rhoeas*), Long headed Poppy (*P. dubium*) and other red poppies

Fruiting capsule galled by two hymenopterans, gall-wasps *Aylax* spp.:

41–3

1. Ovary by **A.** (= *Diplolepis*) **papaveris;**
2. Ovule by **A. minor.**

It is convenient to consider these together: at one time they were regarded as a single species. Both lay their eggs in the developing flower-buds.

A. papaveris colonizes the *septa* between the compartments of the ovary, with the result that these thin partitions undergo enormous development, producing irregular, fleshy extensions which meet and unite and almost completely fill the capsule.

A. minor causes the *ovules* to swell so much that they become united with each other and fill the capsule with a mass of spongy tissue.

Fifty larvae sometimes hatch in a single ovary from infestation by either species. The galls start to grow in June and mature in July–August. Pupation takes place in the capsule, and the adult bites its way through the side wall when it emerges.

These galls are easily missed, since neither necessarily affects the colour or shape of the fruit; although considerable distortion and swelling is sometimes obvious, especially from *A. papaveris*. Imagines can be reared from capsules gathered when these appear to be ripe and either kept over dry sand in a jar or enclosed in a bag of fine-mesh material.

Little reliable information is available about the range or abundance of either species.

CRUCIFERAE, Cabbage family
Brassica

> Swede (*B. napus*)

Stem galled by bacterium, **Agrobacterium** (= *Bacillus, Phytomonas, Pseudomonas*) **tumefaciens.**

'Crown gall.' The causer is a minute bacillus, about 0·002 mm long, known to be capable of infesting representatives of 18–20 families of flowering plants, the majority herbaceous but including some that are woody. The gall itself is very variable in form and size. On a herb, it generally develops on the 'crown', i.e. the hypocotyl at or immediately below the level of the soil. The resultant swelling may attain the size of a pea or expand until it is several centimetres across. In addition to the primary tumour containing the bacteria, secondary tumours devoid of bacteria may develop at a distance from the site of infestation, the primary and its secondaries being connected by strands of specialized cells. Together these growths can bring about considerable distortion.

The causative organism does not produce enzymes capable of dissolving away the cell walls, so that it lives in the existing spaces between the cells instead of forming its own cavities or penetrating the cell interiors. It has marked powers of stimulating cells in its immediate vicinity to divide and form masses of tumour. The substance which stimulates tumour development may be a plant hormone, such as auxin a or auxin b, produced by the host's tissues under the influence of the bacteria and not by the bacteria themselves. It has also been suggested that the reaction is due, not so much to the production of such an auxin as to the removal of some substance which normally inhibits the further division of cells.

The crown-gall tumour was discovered in 1853 and, since then, has been the subject of considerable research stimulated, partly, by apparent affinities between the physiology of this gall and that of cancerous growths in certain animals. Literature is extensive: Mani gives a useful summary.

> Swede
> Cabbage (*B. oleracea*)
> also various cruciferous weeds
> Rootlet galled by slime-fungus **Plas-**
49 modiophora brassicae.

'Finger-and-toe', 'club-root', 'grub', 'anbury'. The causer usually invades side roots rather than the main root, where its activities result in the growth of elongated, finger-like swellings of very varied dimensions, which are quite different from the hemispherical galls brought about by the weevil *Ceuthorhynchus pleurostigma* (Pl. 50). The parasite lives within the vacuoles of the individual cells and its spores are liberated by the decay of the galled tissues. The season is from July to November.

A destructive colonizer in some districts. When a host is attacked early in life, its leaves droop and its root becomes inedible. A suitable treatment for small numbers of plants consists of 'puddling' the drills with a solution of

1 oz of perchloride of mercury in 10 gallons of water, using about ½ pint of the liquid for each brassica. The material is somewhat expensive: the addition of slaked lime to soil tends to reduce infestation and is more suitable for large areas. It is advisable to refrain from growing a cruciferous crop in an infected field for 7 to 8 years after the initial outbreak, and cruciferous weeds should be kept down since many of these serve as potential reservoirs for reinfestation.

> Cabbage
> Swede
> Turnip (*B. rapa*)

Raphanus
> Wild Radish (*R. raphaniastrum*)

Sinapis
> Charlock (*S. arvensis*)

Arabis
> Garden Arabis (*A. caucasica*)
Root galled by coleopteran, weevil
Ceuthorhynchus pleurostigma (= **50**
C. assimilis, *C. sulcicollis*).

'Turnip-and-cabbage gall-weevil.' Probably the most familiar of the larger root galls and one which is sometimes seen on fresh vegetables in food shops. The adult weevils feed on the flower buds. After mating in spring, the female drops to the ground and penetrates the soil to the crown and upper part of the root. Here she excavates cavities in the root with her snout and deposits an egg in each. The plant tissues close over the eggs, and each gall develops as a hemispherical boss, the size of a small marble, which is generally the same colour as the rest of the root. Adjacent swellings may coalesce.

The gall matures in about a month, when the fully grown larva emerges and pupates in the soil close to the surface. Two broods are reared each year, the second developing in autumn.

Widely distributed. Heavy infestation inhibits growth in young plants, and may promote decay of the root system by the entry of fungi and other organisms through the larval holes. Another weevil inducing subterranean galls is *Cleonus piger*, which infests thistles growing in many places near sandy coasts. Its larvae develop in galls on the roots.

Rorippa

Creeping Yellow-cress (*R. sylvestris*)

Sisymbrium

Hedge Mustard (*S. officinale*)

Barbarea

Yellow Rocket (*B. vulgaris*) Shoot apex galled by dipteron, gall-midge **Dasyneura sisymbrii** (= **79** *Cecidomyia sisymbrii, C. barbarea*).

Oviposition results in growth becoming arrested, with the nodes close together and the formation of glossy, more or less globular swellings of variable size in the affected parts, particularly those of flowers. The sepals and petals become swollen at the bases, and the larvae live between such organs, inside the galls but outside the actual plant tissues instead of within special larval chambers. Several galls may be so bunched as to give the appearance of a raspberry fruit. Colours change from cream to pale pink.

Typically, two broods develop in the year: the first from eggs laid in spring, which produce imagines in late summer; and the second from eggs deposited by these, which give rise to the over-wintering brood whose adults appear in May. Pupation takes place in the galls.

Locally plentiful. Infestation of other crucifers is common.

Cabbage
Charlock
Wild Radish

Capsella

Shepherd's Purse (*C. bursa-pastoris*)

Erysium

Treacle Mustard (*E. cheiran-thoides*)

Coronopus

Swine Cress (*C. squamatus*) Shoot galled by fungi, phycomycetes **Albugo** (= *Cystopus*) spp.

'White mould of Cruciferae', 'white blister', 'blister rust'. There are several species of *Albugo*: that infesting shepherd's purse is *A. candida* (*C. candidus*). The fungus invades the host's tissues through the agency either of reproductive bodies (conidia) transported in the air or on the bodies of animals, or else through free-swimming bodies (zoospores). Colonization is effected by hyphae which ramify between the cells of any part of the shoot and insert haustoria into some of them which absorb their contents. One result of the infestation is that giant cells develop here and there within the host's tissues and rapidly undergo fragmentation. Such cells apparently release a substance which stimulates further cell proliferation. Superficially, the gall shows as a blistering and gross distortion of an affected part, which becomes white and powdery as the epidermis ruptures with the pressure of enormous numbers of reproductive bodies developing beneath it.

Generally distributed, but somewhat erratic in its appearance, a wet season particularly favouring the rapid colonization of close-growing plants by zoospores swimming in the water film. Generally, the gall matures in late summer and autumn. The winter is passed as a sexually produced resting stage, which is liberated from the host's tissues when these die, and which can remain viable in the soil for several years.

Albugo may show close relationships with several other colonizers. For example, the mould *Peronospora parasitica* (Pl. 45) frequently occurs intermingled with *Albugo* and seems to colonize a host more successfully if it invades the tissues of this gall. When on its own, it sets up a woolly looking infestation commonly called 'downy mildew'. Aphids sometimes act as agents of dispersal in transferring *Albugo* to fresh hosts, and the mould has been found within aphid galls on certain Cruciferae.

CHENOPODIACEAE, Goosefoot family
Chenopodium
Fat Hen (*Ch. album*)
Atriplex
Common Orache (*A. patula*)
Hastate Orache (*A. hastata*)
Leaf galled by homopteran, aphid
47 Hayhurstia (= *Aphis*) **atriplicis.**

A roll gall, which results from the puncturing of the upper epidermis of the leaf by the feeding aphids. The margins thicken and roll upwards and inwards to meet along the midrib. Galls occur from early summer and attain full size in August, during which time they have passed from yellowish green to light brown and may have reached a length of 4–5 cms.

A mature gall often contains aphids in all stages of development: eggs, nymphs, adult males, wingless oviparous females, and both winged and wingless viviparous females. Evidently

some eggs survive the winter inside the folds of galled leaves after these have become detached from the dying stems. Such leaves may be blown about in the wind and reach a fresh supply of food which the young aphids can exploit when they hatch.

Abundant in many districts. Galls on the upper (narrow) leaves of *Ch. album* are frequently sickle-shaped and closely resemble those of the mite *Eriophyes galii* on *Galium* (Pl. 268).

TILIACEAE, Linden family
Tilia
Common Lime (*T.* × *vulgaris*)
Leaf-blade galled by acarines, gall-mites *Eriophyes* spp.:

1. **E. tiliae typicus** (= *Erineum tiliaceum, Phyllerium tiliaceum, Ceratoneon extensum*);   **56**
2. **E. tiliae exilis;**   **57**
3. **E. tetrastichus** (= *Phytoptus tetrastichus, Legnon crispum*);   **58**
4. **E. leiosoma** (= *E. tiliae leiosoma*).   **59**

Several species of mite parasitize lime leaves and induce galls, and the situation is extremely complex. The following are four which are widely distributed.

1. 'Nail gall', 'bugle gall' (*E. tiliae typicus*). A familiar and striking pouch gall, often particularly numerous on the lower levels of a tree, where as many as 150 may colonize a single leaf, scattered at random over the surface and generally missing the larger veins. Each is a conical structure about 0·8 cm long, erect or oblique and sometimes curved (hence 'bugle gall'), resembling the shaft of a tack protruding through the upper surface of the blade. Occasionally two coalesce at the base, but diverge and form separate apices. Although the exterior is

hairy at first, its upper part becomes smooth and shiny, but hairs persist near the base, some appear as a patch on the lower epidermis immediately underneath the gall, and its interior is filled with long hairs among which the causers occur in great numbers.

Coloration ranges from greenish yellow to crimson and brown. Development begins in June, the galls mature in July–August, and persist until leaf-gall.

2. *E. tiliae exilis.* Instead of being arranged hapazardly, the galls are restricted to the angles between the larger veins (compare *E. axillare* on *Alnus*; although colonization by the present

a   b   c

d   e   f

Fig. 4. Six examples of leaf galls of eriophyid mites zoned relative to venation. *Top*, galls restricted to angles between midrib and major veins: a – *E. axillare* (alder), p. 144; b – *E. lionotus* (birch), p. 144; c – *E. pulchellum* (hornbeam), p. 146. *Bottom*, galls along lateral veins: d – *E. tiliae exilis* (lime), p. 122; e – *E. macrochelus* (maple), p. 124; f – *E. nervisequus* (beech), p. 148.

species extends beyond the midrib, to include the angles between the secondary and tertiary veins). It is exceptional to find more than 50 galls on one leaf. Each is normally a hemispherical pouch, 0·2 cm across, out-pocketed from the upper surface and covered with hairs ,which also form conspicuous tawny patches on the lower surface and fill the interior. Its colour changes from greenish yellow to dark red and brown. Sometimes elongated specimens occur, with the vertical sides parallel and a domed top. The season is much the same as for *typicus* (no. 1).

3. *E. tetrastichus.* Infestation is typically of the leaf margin, and results in the formation of a roll gall. The serrations are first attacked, when they curve and touch the upper surface, and the rolling is then continued until it extends all round the leaf with a small, puckered area left in the middle. The exterior is slightly hairy, the interior more so, and dimensions very variable: the colour ranges from green to redbrown. Development begins in June and the galls mature in September.

The same causer may affect the flat part of the blade, inducing small pouch galls on the upper surface.

4. *E. leiosoma.* The least impressive of the four galls. It consists essentially of a roughened patch, affecting both upper and lower surfaces alike, bearing hairs among which the mites live and reproduce. Initially white, it passes through red to brown. Specimens occur from May onwards.

Common Lime

Leaf-blade galled by dipterons, gallmidges *Dasyneura* spp.:

61   1. **D.** (= *Perrisia*) **tiliamvolvens;**

0–1   2. **D. thomasiana.**

Both causers bring about the forma-

tion of leaf-margin galls, in which the edge rolls upon the upper surface of the blade and encloses several cream or pink larvae. When galls are in juxtaposition, the margin presents a scalloped appearance, each roll being about 2·0 cm long, and the centre of the blade may become puckered and bear small blotches. Initially green, the roll soon darkens to purplish brown. Galls develop between the end of May and August, and the colonizers pupate in the soil.

Simple distinctions concern the texture of the rolled wall. That of *D. thomasiana* is thickened and somewhat leathery, with hairs abnormally developed on both the inner and outer surfaces. The *D. tiliamvolvens* wall is not visibly thickened and produces a leaf crinkle, but is stiff enough to resist uncurling, the rigidity being due to sheets of strengthening cells laid down between the leaf veins. Its surface is no more hairy than the rest of the leaf.

D. tiliamvolvens is the commoner of the two.

Common Lime

Leaf-petiole, midrib, young stem or inflorescence galled by dipteron, gallmidge **Contarinia tiliarum** (= *Cecidomyia tiliae, Ce. excavans, Ce. floricola, Ce. limbivolens, Sciara tilicola*).   **62–4**

The gall commonly develops at the distal end of the petiole, just below the leaf-blade, and takes the form of a globular, sessile swelling, 1·0 cm across. Frequently, the underside of the midrib is swollen. If there is colonization of the stem, this occurs in the new season's growth at, or very near, one of the nodes. It tends particularly to grow among the dense mass of young shoots arising from the base of a trunk, when it is conspicuous both on account of its low position and its bright red colouring when mature. Eventually, the gall turns black.

The larval chambers (up to 20) are situated in the zone of vascular bundles. Cells of the cortex increase in size and number, and the vascular bundles near each chamber also become larger. Should the petiole be galled, two side-effects are often observed:

1. There is inhibition of the tissues beyond the swelling, so that the leaf-blade fails to develop normally;

2. The stunted leaf becomes very hairy and a site for colonization by a range of other gall organisms, including dipterons and mites.

Growth begins in May–June, development is complete by late July, pupation takes place in the gall and the imagines emerge in August.

Fairly widespread. Mature galls can be reared if twigs bearing them are removed, their ends placed in water and the galled parts enclosed in a bag.

Common Lime

Leaf-blade galled by dipteron, gall-midge **Didymomyia reamuriana.**

65–71

The larvae of this dipteron induce galls which, particularly before maturity, are conspicuous. Thirty or 40 may occur together, mainly between the petiole and the leaf centre and missing the larger veins. Each is a pustule, 0·4 cm across, involving both surfaces of the blade, rising to a cone 0·3 cm high on one surface (usually the upper) and to a hemisphere 0·2 cm high on the other. Frequently some galls coalesce, imparting a lumpy appearance to the leaf. The colour of the galls themselves is greenish yellow, but in the early stages a bright red stain spreads outwards from their bases well into the surrounding tissues, so that when an infested leaf is viewed by transmitted light the effect is striking even from a distance—a red 'pool' surrounding clear, circular 'islands'.

Unilocular and unilarval. The gall develops a hard, cylindrical, inner core as it grows which springs off from the softer tissues at maturity, carrying within it the full-grown larva and leaving a crater-like aperture with a lip 0·2 cm in diameter, on one surface and a smaller opening on the other. Numbers of these fallen cylinders may be found in July lying on the soil beneath an infested tree. The edge of the escape-pore is red-brown, fine brownish lines radiate from the centre, and the peripheral red colour in the blade largely disappears, persisting only as a narrow brownish surround in the immediate vicinity of each gall. This phase generally coincides with the development of the globular fruits of the host, and the galls tend to be missed when viewed among clusters of these.

Reliable information is lacking on several aspects of the natural history of this causer, although the imago is not difficult to rear. Galls evidently develop between early May and mid-July, after which it becomes hard to find larval occupants. The species appears to be local and, indeed, may be absent altogether from some districts where lime trees grow in abundance.

ACERACEAE, Maple family
Acer

Common Maple (*A. campestre*) Leaf-blade galled by acarine, gall-mite **Eriophyes macrochelus** (= *Aceria macrochela typica, Phytoptus macrochelus, Ph. moniezi, Erineum purpurascens, Cephaloneon solitarium*). Fig 4 (e). 72 Although variable, the gall is distinguished from that of *E. macrorhynchus cephalodes* by its form, position, colour, density and texture. It is either solitary or coalesced, more or less globular or reniform in shape, 0·3–0·6 cm in diameter, with thick, woody walls and generally slightly downy. Colouring may be greenish, orange or red-brown. It develops on the upper surface of the leaf, in the angle between one of the primary veins radiating from the petiole and a secondary vein. The number on a single leaf rarely exceeds 100 and is usually much less.

Specimens can be found between June and November and growth is complete in August–September. Widespread in southern and central districts of England, but not as common as *macrorhynchus*. Another subspecies, *Aceria macrochela heteronyx*, is said to cause bark galls on the same host.

Sycamore (*A. pseudoplatanus*)
Leaf-blade galled by acarine, gall-mite
4 Eriophyes megalonyx.

The mite induces pouches in the blade which appear on the underside as concave, hairy blotches, light brown in colour, and on the upper surface as green, yellowish or red-brown convexities. Dimensions are very variable.

Specimens may be found throughout most of the time the tree is in leaf, but darkening of the colour only takes place from late summer onwards.

Common Maple
Sycamore
Leaf-blade galled by acarine, gall-mite
7 3 Eriophyes macrorhynchus ssp. (= **-6** *Aceria macrorhyncha typica, Ceratoneon vulgare, Phytoptus macrorhynchus*) and including **Aceria macrorhyncha cephalonea** (= *Cephaloneon myriadeum, Phytoptus myriadeum*).

The toxonomy of the galls induced on sycamore and maple by mites is complex. Nalepa A. 1929, *Marcellia* 25 : 119, distinguishes two kinds of pocket galls on sycamore alone. Here we are deliberately simplifying matters by treating as a single species the causer of the familiar red shiny pustules on both maple and sycamore: *Eriophyes macrorhynchus cephalodes* on maple and *E. macrorhynchus aceribus* on sycamore.

A densely gregarious colonizer, between 500 and 1,000 galls frequently developing on a single leaf, generally on the upper surface. Each consists of a glossy, hemispherical pimple, 0·1 cm high, enclosing a cavity bearing elongated, unicellular hairs. The colour range is from greenish yellow to dark red and purple. Growth begins in June, the galls mature in early autumn and persist until the leaves fall.

Colonization seems particularly to affect the lower branches of sycamore and maple grown as hedgerow shrubs. Widespread wherever the hosts are abundant.

Several inquiline mites are common in galls on both species of plant.

AQUIFOLIACEAE, Holly family
Ilex
Holly (*I. aquifolium*) including variegated var.
Leaf-blade galled by dipteran, agromyzid **Phytomyza ilicis.** 77

The larva mines into the holly leaf and is remarkable in that its activities, unlike those of most leaf-miners, result in the development of a simple type of gall instead of the colonized leaf merely remaining passive. The parasite feeds on the chlorophyllous cells immediately underneath the upper epidermis. Uninjured cells below these then divide and form multi-layered, elongated, tubular masses which grow into the cavity of the mine and set up a pressure which causes the epidermis to become bulged and bladder-like. Evidently the stimulus here is simply that of mechanical injury, and there seems to be no direct connection with the insect's feeding activities as such.

Development starts in spring. The form of the mine is more irregular than some, but it consists typically of a median chamber with a series of rounded bays of varying sizes pushing outwards from its periphery, like the pseudopodia of *Amoeba*. Much of it is greenish or yellowish white, although the centre of an older mine generally carries brown or purple flecks and stains. Pupation takes place in the mine, and the imago leaves around midsummer through an aperture in the epidermis, about 0·15 cm across, ringed by a purple areola. If the epidermis is stripped off with a knife-blade, the empty pupal skin can be seen immediately behind this hole and, under a hand lens, the droppings of the larva among the tubular groups of proliferated cells projecting upwards from the floor of the mine into its cavity. Empty mines can be found throughout the year, as they remain until the affected leaves fall off, and a holly leaf normally persists for twelve months or more.

This is an interesting and particularly easy dipteron to rear. In some localities it is so abundant that long hedges of holly bordering gardens have up to a third of their leaves infested. Among other common insects with leaf-mining larvae which, indirectly, cause similar galls, are the dipteron *Pegomyia chenopodii* on fat hen (*Chenopodium album*) and upright goosefoot (*Ch. urbicum*), and the weevil *Rhynchaenus quercus* on oak (*Quercus* sp.).

BUXACEAE, Box family
Buxus

Box (*B. sempervirens*)

Terminal bud galled by homopteran, psyllid **Psylla buxi.**

'Box cabbage gall.' The infested bud forms a yellowish green, leafy, globular structure, about 2·0 cm across, closely resembling a tiny cabbage. The outer leaves thicken and enclose the inner, growing ones, from which the psyllids derive their food. As is usual with psyllids, only a few insects occur in a single gall. Their nymphs also attack some of the non-clustered leaves behind the growing point, inducing a degree of yellowing, distortion and a certain amount of thickening in the form of blister-like irregularities on the blades. Nymphs are commonly seen partly enveloped in the débris of moulted skins.

Galls may be found throughout the year, but appear to be active between May and October. So long as the insects continue to feed, no new length develops, but buds sometimes grow out after they have left.

Widespread and often very abundant, both on wild and cultivated shrubs.

LEGUMINOSAE (subfamily
PAPILIONACEAE), **Peaflower
family**
Lupinus

Lupin (*L. nootkatensis*)

Trifolium

Clover (*T.* spp.)

and Papilionates generally

Root galled by bacteria, e.g. **Rhizobium** (=*Bacillus*) **beyerinckii** on 52 *Lupinus* and **R.** (=*B.*) **radicicola** on 53 other papilionates.

Root-nodule galls caused by bacteria

on members of the family Leguminosae are among the best known of those induced by true soil organisms, as opposed to causers like some of the aphids and gall-wasps, which spend much of their lives above ground. The bacteria (Fig. 5) penetrate the root-hairs and epidermis and multiply near

cocci

banded rods

y form

Fig. 5. Polymorphic bacterium of genus *Rhizobium* causing root-nodules on roots of legumes (× 500).

the point of entry, with the result that swelling of various shapes and sizes develop through proliferation of the cortical cells. Eventually the bacterial zone within the root becomes separated from the rest of the tissues by a surrounding sheath of starch cells. Details of the anatomy and developmental phases are relatively complex.

Such galls differ from most of those

considered here in not being wholly parasitic. The bacteria benefit the galled plant by combining nitrogen in the soil air with carbohydrates manufactured by the plant, thus bringing about the first stages in the synthesis of protein material which becomes assimilated by the host. The increase in the amount of nitrogen 'fixed' in this way is a reason for including such plants as clovers in a crop rotation, when one of the courses consists of a 'nitrogen-greedy' crop like a cereal.

To all intents and purposes, the galls are universally distributed.

Galls of *radicicola* on clover etc. seem frequently to become a particular site of attack for the root-feeding larvae of *Sitona* weevils. The larvae of the small 'stilt-legged fly' *Tylos corrigiolatus* also live within the bacterial nodules on clover.

White Clover (*T. repens*)
Inflorescence galled possibly by acarine, gall-mite. **80–1**
An example of a phyllanthous (= 'leaf-flower') gall, in which certain floral structures become replaced by green foliage. In the present case, the male parts (stamens) of each flower develop in the usual way as 10 anthers supported on filaments ensheathed by a tube. The female parts (ovary, style and stigma) fail to mature. Instead, the tissues from which they would normally arise greatly enlarge, rupture the stamen-tube from the inside, and what emerges from the flower-head is a cluster of miniature, trifid leaves similar in their basic structure to the ordinary photosynthetic leaves on the vegetative shoots.

The actual cause of phyllanthy in *T. repens* is still being disputed, some authorities maintaining that it is the result of virus infection, although the majority opinion would seem to be in favour of mite attack. Eelworms have also been suggested as possible causers. A planned investigation into the problem would form a useful subject for a project.

Probably widespread but spasmodic. The phenomenon requires further study in all its aspects. Flowering plants of other species are subject to similar distortion, particularly such Compositae as ox-eye daisy (*Chrysanthemum leucanthemum*) when proliferation may include the development of a secondary capitulum.

White Clover

Leaflet galled by dipteron, gall-midge
82–3 Dasyneura (= *Cecidomyia*) **trifolii.**

This bears a general resemblance to the midge gall on a rose leaflet caused by *Wachtiella rosarum*, Pl. 95. The leaflet is folded longitudinally, the margins are closely pressed together to form a hollow pod, and the outside is the original lower epidermis. The positions occupied by the larvae are indicated by small swellings. Colours range from green, through yellow, to red-brown. The size is about $1·2 \times 0·4$ cm.

A plurilocular and multilarval structure. The insects escape when the margins separate and pupation is in the soil. The season extends from June to October.

Genista

Dyer's Greenweed (*G. tinctoria*)
Terminal leaves galled by dipteron,
84 gall-midge Jaapiella genisticola (= *Perrisia genisticola, Asphondylia genistae*).

Structurally, the gall is typical of such modifications as those produced on yew by *Taxomyia taxi*, Pl. 32, 33 juniper by *Oligotrophus juniperinus*,

Pl. 31 and reed by *Lipara lucens*, Pl. 290–1 in all of which elongation at the growing tip is arrested, internodes are suppressed so that the terminal leaves become bunched, and there is an increase in the cortex, vascular tissue, etc. The present species is sometimes plentiful in large patches of the plant, where the gall can be seen to be oval or globular, about $1·0$ cm across, greenish yellow or brown in colour, to consist of aggregated leaves which are pilose on the outside, and sometimes to involve aborted flowers.

The larvae are readily discovered if the outer leaves are peeled off. They feed upon the inner ones. Galls may be found between June and October and are mature in September.

Sarothamnus

Broom (*S. scoparius*)
Leaf-bud or fruit galled by dipteron,
gall-midge **Asphondylia sarothamni** 8
(= *A. mayri*).

An 'ambrosia gall' in which there appears to be a close relationship between an insect causer and a fungus, but not one where the fungus provides the causer with food.

The bud gall develops as a pink or reddish oval structure, with a conical, pale green apex, and is about 1 cm long. Unilocular and unilarval: the insect occupies the lower part of the gall chamber in the early stages, with the hyphae of a fungus visible in the upper part. Eventually the fungus spreads downwards and forms a layer which separates the larva from the surrounding gall. Nevertheless, the insect appears to derive its nourishment from the tissues of the broom and not from those of the fungus, since it develops normally even when, as occasionally happens, the fungus fails to grow. So long as the larva is feeding actively, the gall cells continue to proliferate and the fungus is held in check and feeds as a saprophyte on dead matter. But as soon as the insect stops eating prior to pupating, the gall ceases to grow and the fungus becomes luxuriant and fills the cavity, and the insect pupates in the dense mass of hyphae. The fungus becomes a parasite on the gall, ramifying between its living cells, sending haustoria (suckers) into them, and extracting food material. The adult insect emerges in May–June.

Emergence at this time coincides with the availability of flowers, and eggs may be laid in these. The resulting gall forms on the wall of the pod, generally near the pedicel, and is an elongated, pale green, unilarval structure, about 1 cm long and 0·5 cm broad. The fungus also occurs in this and appears to undergo similar changes to those noted in the bud gall. By the time the adult midges leave the fruit galls in late summer, flowering is over, and their eggs are deposited in leaf buds.

The fruit gall is generally less plentiful than the bud form (to which the specific name *mayri* used to be given before the connection between the two was established). Inhabitants are difficult to raise from either type unless the galls are collected immediately before the insects are due to appear.

Lotus
    Bird's-foot Trefoil (*L. corniculatus*).
Vicia
    Bush Vetch (*V. sepium*), Common Vetch (*V. sativa*), etc.

Flower-bud or leaf-bud galled by dipteron, gall-midge **Contarinia** (= *Diplosis, Cecidomyia*) **loti.**　　**87**

On *Lotus*, galls are probably commoner in the flower than in the leaf-buds, whereas the situation seems to be reversed on *Vicia*.

When a flower becomes galled, 5 larvae are usually present in each of a cluster of eight galls, inducing considerable distortion of the bases of the petals and sepals and preventing the bud from opening. Localized distortion of the stamens and female parts are merely secondary effects of these changes in the perianth. A somewhat downy, conical gall, about 1·2 cm long, its colour passing from green, through yellow, to pink and reddish brown. It appears in June, matures in August–September, and the larvae pupate and over-winter in the soil, emerging as adults in the following year.

When vetch foliage is galled, there may be as many as twelve leaflets infested on one rachis. In each case the margins of the leaflet rise above the midrib until they meet and form a fat hollow pod containing 5–6 larvae. The midrib itself becomes swollen and curved, and the elongation of the rachis is inhibited so that the galled leaflets become crowded. The pods are crescentic, and the overall impression is that of an inverted bunch of diminutive bananas, each about 0·8 × 1·5 cm. Colouring is not as bright as when the flower is colonized, and the leaflet galls are generally greenish yellow or brownish.

Fairly plentiful on *Vicia* growing along roadside margins, but in the writer's experience it is exceptional to find dense colonization, even where the host plants are numerous and close together.

Pisum

Culinary Pea (*P. sativum*)

Aerial parts galled by nematode, eel-
88 worm **Tylenchus devastatrix.**

Any structures arising from the buds can be infested, when irregularities of growth cause the plant to assume bizarre shapes: e.g. stem thickened and branched, or exceptionally thin and unbranched; pods contorted, or thin and straight; flowers bunched, or aborted altogether and the entire plant conspicuously stunted. Young eel-worms develop rapidly in the affected parts and soon become a pest, spreading rapidly from the diseased to the adjacent healthy plants.

The species was first noticed in England about 1885. It is typical of parasitic nematodes which gall the entire aerial structures of their hosts, such as *Tylenchus dipsaci* on grasses, *Aphelenchus fragariae* on strawberry (*Fragaria vesca*) and *A. olesistus longicollis* on sweet violet (*Viola odorata*).

ROSACEAE, Rose family
Filipendula

Meadowsweet (*F. ulmaria*)

Leaflet-blade galled by dipteron,
gall-midge **Dasyneura** (=*Perrisia*)
89 **ulmariae.**

The gall shows as a small, reddish pustule on the upper surface of the blade. A single leaflet may carry up to 200 galls. When mature (late July), the gall projects in a cone 0·2–0·4 cm high and is covered with silky hairs. Unilocular and unilarval. Pupation takes place within the gall itself, the

apex of which is detached and pushed aside by the imago when it emerges in August.

So abundant in some districts that practically every plant is infested to some extent.

Rubus

Bramble (*R. fruticosus*)
Dewberry (*R. caesius*)

Stem galled by:
  1. dipteron, gall-midge **Lasioptera rubi** (=*L. argyrosticta*, *L. picta*, *L. fusca*);
  2. hymenopteran, gall-wasp **Diastrophus rubi** (=*Andricus hartigi*).

Two galls which take the form of swellings in the stem and are sometimes confused.

1. *Lasioptera rubi*. Usually asymmetrical, developing as a swelling on one side of the stem near the tip. Occasionally it appears on the leaf petiole, where it is probably always unsuccessful. Eggs are laid in spring and the rapid proliferation of the inner tissues ruptures the epidermis so that the gall becomes lumpy and rough-looking. By September, the structure has attained full size and become reddish brown. Its dimensions vary considerably. Unilocular and multilarval: the larvae over-winter in the gall, pupate there and the adults appear in April–May.

One of the so-called 'ambrosia galls'. Instead of feeding directly upon the tissues of the host, the larvae derive nourishment from the mycelium of an ambrosia fungus, introduced by the midge herself at the time of egg-laying, which becomes established within the gall.

Colonization is usually of branches

deep inside bramble scrub, so that the galls are harder to locate than those of the next species, which tend to grow on more superficial parts.

2. *Diastrophus rubi.* Occasional on raspberry (*Rubus idaeus*), but commonest on bramble. Colonization is of the new growth in stems while this is still soft and green. Both prostrate and upright stems may be infested, especially the former, and the galls frequently occur low down in hedgerows or in woodland clearings, partly concealed by herbaceous vegetation. Oviposition is in spring. The affected regions become swollen, curved and bear comparatively few prickles. During the summer, the galls pass from greenish yellow, through pink and purple, to light brown, and attain full size in October–November. Plurilocular: a large specimen (15 cm long) may contain 80–200 larvae. Pupation occurs in the galls and the imagines emerge the following spring. After they have left, the epidermis flakes off and the structures become dark brown and woody. Old galls are persistent—specimens perforated with exit-holes may be found at any season.

Parasites are frequent, five species being particularly common.

Both the *Lasioptera* and *Diastrophus* galls are difficult to rear since growth ceases when they are removed from the parent plant and the tissues soon become so contracted and hardened that either the larvae cannot pupate or the imagines cannot escape. Success may follow if the galls are cut from the bushes in March or early April, immediately before the adults are due to emerge, or if lengths of infested stem are transplanted in soil. Immersion of the cut ends of stems in water is usually unsuccessful.

Potentilla

Creeping Cinquefoil (*P. reptans*)

Rhizome or petiole galled by hymenopteran, gall-wasp **Xestophanes potentillae** (= *Cynips potentillae*, *Aylax potentillae*, *A. abbreviatus*, *A. splendens*).

Oviposition occurs in June and commonly affects the rhizome close to the soil surface. Eggs inserted in the petiole result in spindle-shaped swellings, often thicker on one side of the leaf-stalk than another, distributed singly or in twos and threes at irregular intervals, and resembling small beads threaded on a string. At first succulent and greenish or pink in colour, they later become hard and brown. There are commonly six larval cells in a continuous swelling some 2·0 cm long. Each lies centrally within the vascular bundles, to which it is connected by minute channels, so that some nourishment may be derived directly from them. The galls appear in July, become mature in October, the larvae pupate and overwinter in them, and the imagines make their escape in the following spring.

Xestophanes brevitarsis (= *X. tormentillae*) causes galls on the aerial branches of common tormentil (*P. erecta*), but these tend to be more coalescent and to contain more larval cells.

These are interesting hymenopterans to rear, although failure is likely if the galled structures are severed from the main plant in summer or autumn and placed in water. Specimens should either be removed in winter, when pupation has taken place, or entire galled plants dug up, transferred to pots of soil and kept indoors.

Rosa

Field Rose (*R. arvensis*)
Dog Rose (*R. canina*)

Leaflet galled by:

95
1. dipteron, gall-midge **Wachtiella rosarum** (=*Cecidomyia rosarum, C. rosae*);

96
2. hymenopteran, sawfly **Blennocampa pusilla.**

1. *Wachtiella rosarum.* The gall comprises a single leaflet folded along its midrib, with the margins tightly adpressed to form a neat, hollow pod, of which the exterior is the original under surface. The blade of the leaflet is slightly thickened and, in older galls, generally tinged red-brown. Approximate size, 3·0 × 1·5 cm.

Unilocular, containing up to 50 larvae. Development begins in June and maturity is reached in August–September, when the margins gape and allow the larvae to fall to the ground to pupate. Many larvae quit immature galls which are detached from the plant. Imagines emerge in about a week after pupation.

Gregarious, many infested leaflets usually occurring together. This particular species is not very common, but it is certainly not the only cause of such pod-like folding in rose leaflets. Similar galls are induced on clover leaflets by the dipteron *Dasyneura trifolii.* Pl. 82–3.

2. *Blennocampa pusilla.* Curvatures caused by this little black sawfly are quite distinctive, the leaflet being rolled downwards instead of being folded upwards, so that the exterior is the original upper surface. It presents a more untidy, withered appearance, and the long axis of the gall is frequently twisted to some extent. The larvae, too, are easily distinguished: those of the sawfly are caterpillar-like, with

feet, while the dipterous larvae are legless maggots. The sawfly gall is the earlier of the two to mature.

Field Rose
Dog Rose

Leaflet, rachis, sepal or stem galled by hymenopterans, gall-wasps *Diplolepis* spp.:

1. **D.** (=*Rhodites, Hololexis*) **eglanteriae;** 9

2. **D. nervosus** (=*D. rosarum, Rhodites rosarum, Rh. nervosus*); 9

3. **D. spinosissimae.**

1. *D. eglanteriae.* 'Smooth pea gall.' Primarily a colonizer of leaf structures, including the surface of the bedeguar (*D. rosae*), another leaf gall. It most frequently develops on the underside of a leaflet. Often solitary, but as many as 15 may be present on one compound leaf. About 0·5 cm in diameter, globular and usually smooth, but sometimes bearing depressions or minute tubercles, the unilocular and unilarval gall first appears in July and becomes fully developed in September–October, meanwhile passing from pale green to rose-red. It falls to the ground in autumn, the causer pupates within it, and the adult emerges in spring.

Several parasites and inquilines are known.

A locally distributed gall, but it tends to be overlooked. This is due partly to its concealed position and also to its spherical shape and deepening colour confusing the eyes when it is viewed among ripening hips.

If the branches are carefully turned back to expose the undersides of the leaflets, a considerable number of galls can sometimes be found within a short time. Occupants are easily reared from material gathered in autumn.

2. *D. nervosus*. 'Spiked pea gall.' Unmistakable on account of the long spines, one to six in number, projecting from the surface and giving the impression of a diminutive naval mine. Size, about 0·5 cm diameter; and colour range from yellowish green, through pink, to brown.

The same general features apply to this gall as to that of *eglanteriae*, but it seems to be commoner. Its spines tend to make it inconspicuous on a prickly bush.

3. *D. spinosissimae* colonizes burnet rose (*R. pimpinellifolia*) as well as other *Rosa* species (including *R. canina*). Its spherical galls are internal, in the leaf midrib or petiole, and do not erupt through the epidermis. Locally common.

Field Rose
Dog Rose

Leaflet, rachis or sepal galled by hymenopteran, gall-wasp **Diplolepis rosae** (=*D. bedeguaris, Rhodites rosae, Cynips rosae*). Fig. 6.

'Bedeguar gall', 'moss gall', 'Robin's pincushion'. A well-known and exceptionally beautiful gall. In spring the female lays eggs in unopened buds, and colonization is generally of some kind of leaf structure, which proliferates into an aggregation of up to 60 unilarval chambers surrounded by a dense mass of branched and sticky filaments. These give the impression of a ball of moss, and are often brightly coloured, passing from green, through pink and crimson, to reddish brown. Very variable in size: a large specimen may attain a diameter of 10 cm. The gall is at its most attractive in September: thereafter it blackens and loses some of its fibres; but the larvae over-winter and pupate in it, the adults emerging in May.

Occupants can be reared successfully from galls cut from the bushes at the end of winter, when feeding is complete, and kept over sand in jars at room temperature. Many bedeguars yield parasites and inquilines. Of the actual causers which emerge, less than one per cent are likely to be males, and reproduction is mostly by parthenogenetic eggs. Alternation of generations is unknown.

As in many hymenopteran galls, a complex community of other hymenoptera sometimes develops. Several inquilines have been recorded. One of these is the gall-wasp *Periclistus*, which actually causes no gall but deposits eggs in the existing bedeguar tissues. Its larvae may be devoured by a chalcid wasp, *Eurytoma*, which works its way from one inquiline cell to the next. Several parasites—ichnemons and chalcids—lay their eggs directly in the larvae or pupae of the causer and kill them. One of these, the chalcid wasp *Oligosthenus*, may attack both the larvae of the causer and of the inquiline. Such parasites, in turn, are liable to attack by hyperparasites, of which the chalcids *Habrocytus bedeguaris* and *H. periclisti* are examples. Evidently the mossy outgrowths surrounding the gall-core are ineffectual in stopping inquilines, predators, parasites and hyperparasites from entering and locating their precise food-supply. These relationships are represented schematically in Fig. 6.

The tissues of the gall are frequently attacked far more heavily by the parasitic fungus *Phragmidium subcorticum* than are the other parts of the rose bush.

It is not surprising that so mysterious an object should have become a particular focus of superstition and

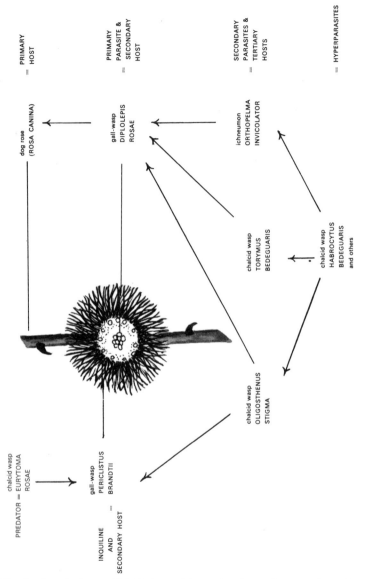

Fig. 6. Rose bedeguar (*Diplolepis rosae*) (p. 133): schema showing relationships between some of the organisms within the gall community. Each arrow points from a feeder to its food.

folk-lore. The countryman's name 'Robin's pincushion' is very old and refers to the woodland sprite Robin Goodfellow. Formerly the gall was gathered and used medicinally—bedeguar tea was supposed to cure diarrhoea in cattle.

An allied form, *D. mayri*, induces galls more sparsely covered in short, unbranched spines. These usually develop on twigs. Several *Rosa* species are colonized, including *R. canina*. Rare.

Prunus

> Blackthorn (*P. spinosa*)
> Bullace (*P. domestica* var. *insititia*)

Leaf blade galled by acarine, gall-mite **3 Eriophyes** (= *Phytoptus*) **similis.**

Frequently, blackthorn is so heavily colonized that a single leaf may carry up to 60 galls and be greatly deformed. Growths are usually thickest around the margin. Each is a more or less oval structure, measuring 0·50 × 0·30 cm, projecting more from the upper than the lower surface, and of a yellowish, orange or purple colour. Crowded galls tend to coalesce. The aperture is irregular in shape and fringed with minute hairs. If the opened gall is examined under a lens, it can be seen to carry hairs of two distinct kinds, on the outside and inside respectively.

Galls generally appear in May and become mature in August–September. An abundant species in many localities.

> Blackthorn
> Bullace
> Plum (*P. domestica* var. *domestica*)

Fruit galled by fungus, ascomycete **5 Taphrina pruni** (= *Ascomyces pruni*, *Exoascus pruni*, *E. insititiae*).

'Bladder bullace', 'pocket plum',

'starved plum', 'mock plum'. The fungus becomes established in the developing fruit, where it causes flattening and elongation, prevents the formation of the kernel and renders the pericarp inedible. The corrugated surface becomes covered with the fungal hyphae, and the colour ranges from pale green, through greyish, to dusty orange. It develops in June, attains full size in July and persists until September. The dimensions are very variable: a large specimen may be 6 cm long.

Closely related fungi cause similar galls on other *Prunus* species, such as bird-cherry (*P. padus*), as well as infesting the foliage of almond. Widespread. In many cases colonization is dense and eradication difficult.

> Almond (*P. amygdalus*)
> Peach (*P. persica*)
> Nectarine (*P. persica* var. *nectarina*)

Leaf-blade galled by fungus, ascomycete. **Taphrina** (= *Exoascus*) **defor- 106 mans.**

'Peach-leaf curl.' The fungus causes the leaf to swell out into baggy pouches, all more or less large, and often so close together that the entire blade is crumpled. On examining the interior, however, it is common to find the base near the petiole, or the distal end, enveloped within the pouching without being infested. The blade is thickened and succulent; the inner surface smooth and shiny and the outer surface, where the spores are being produced, dull matt. Affected leaves frequently develop an attractive reddish hue before eventually darkening to a muddy purple, and many fall prematurely.

So high a proportion of the leaves on a tree may become galled that flowering or fruiting ceases altogether. Compared with those in many pouch galls, the successori tend to be low in numbers and species.

A widespread colonizer, related to the fungus causing mock plum on bullace, blackthorn, etc.

> Gean (*P. avium*)
> Sour Cherry (*P. cerasus*)
> Bird-cherry (*P. padus*)

Terminal leaves galled by homopteran,
107 aphid **Myzus cerasi.**

Colonization of the apical bud of a twig by an over-wintering female results in considerable distortion of the leaves arising from it, which become folded, crumpled and thickened and develop reddish excrescences. The gall generally matures before mid-June.

The summer broods of the aphid fly to such herbaceous plants as bedstraws (*Galium* spp.) and speedwells (*Veronica* spp.), where they feed and reproduce without causing galls.

Crataegus
> Common Hawthorn (*C. monogyna*)
> Midland Hawthorn (*C. oxycanthoides*)

Leaf galled by acarine, gall-mite
108 **Eriophyes goniothorax typicus** (= *Phytoptus goniothorax, Erineum clandestinum, E. oxyacanthae*).

A marginal roll gall, in which the leaf edges curl downwards and roll across the undersurface until, occasionally, the opposite sides meet, when the leaf lobe becomes transformed into a spike. Size variable, but the average diameter of a roll is probably about 0·2 cm. The interior is filled with dense hairs, but externally it resembles the colour and texture of the rest of the leaf. The galls begin to develop as soon as the leaves

unfold, and are mature by September–October.

Widespread, both on woodland and hedgerow trees. Generally not more than six edges of any one leaf are attacked.

> Common Hawthorn
> Midland Hawthorn

Leaf-blade galled by homopteran, aphid **Dysaphis ranunculi.**

A somewhat local gall, which seems nowhere to be very plentiful, but which, when mature, frequently shows up against the normal leaves as a fairly conspicuous object because of its bright tints. Infestation results in the development of a curved, slightly fleshy and sparsely hairy pouch gall, involving either a single lobe or the entire leaf-blade. Dimensions vary considerably, but 2·0 cm seems to be the average length when one lobe is affected. Colours range from greenish yellow, through buff and pink, to russet, and tend to be blotchy. Freshly gathered material soon withers and turns dark brown.

The galls appear particularly to occur in the shadier parts of trimmed hedges. Dense colonization is exceptional. They first show in May, but the aphids have generally flown to herbaceous plants by late June, when only their cast skins remain, adhering to the inner wall of the pouch. After the causers have left, the empty structure may become colonized by a particularly varied range of successori—mites, thrips, earwigs, caterpillars, ants, spiders and chelifers have all been recorded from old galls along 2 metres of hedgerow in a garden at Great Malvern, Worcestershire, and the subject is one providing interesting opportunities for further investigation.

The elm gall bug (*Anthocoris gallarum-ulmi*), which is common as a predator in the galls of the aphid *Eriosoma ulmi* on elm, occasionally attacks the present causer.

Common Hawthorn
Midland Hawthorn

Terminal leaves galled by dipteron, gall-midge **Dasyneura** (=*Perrisia*, *Cecidomyia*) **crataegi.**

A rosette gall. Infestation in March–April of the terminal bud inhibits elongation of the shoot, and the gall consists of eight to forty closely packed leaves, deformed, thickened, with reduced petioles and with greenish or reddish outgrowths scattered over their surfaces. Numerous light red larvae feed and shelter among the leaves and, when full-grown in September–October, fall to the ground to pupate, the adults emerging in spring. Although unable to pupate many larvae quickly leave galls which are gathered before maturity.

Occasionally on isolated shrubs, but more typical as a widespread hedgerow species. New twigs developing after hedge trimming are often densely colonized, the galls appearing conspicuous on topmost shoots viewed against the sky. Old galls are persistent, the elongation of affected branches continuing from buds behind the tips.

In mature galls, leaves well behind the main cluster are frequently distorted and bear pustules or ligulate excrescences. 'Ringing' experiments would be instructive here. By selecting galls in early stages of development and peeling off the outer tissues all round the stem immediately behind them in a narrow band down to the wood, it might be possible to discover whether such distortion is due to a chemical translocated along the phloem from the site of infestation and affecting the leaves after they have expanded. (Water and salts would continue to reach the terminal foliage via the sapwood.)

Pyrus

Pear (*P. communis*)

Leaf-blade galled by acarine, gall-mite **Eriophyes pyri** (=*Phytoptus arianus*, *P. arionae*, *P. pyri*, *Typhlodromus pyri*). **113**

'Pear-leaf blister.' One of the commonest galls of its type—a biconvex swelling of the leaf-blade developed equally on both sides, about 0·2 cm across. The causative mites occur among the cells forming the solid core of the gall and seem to gain entry through the stomata, later expanding these to pores on the undersurface large enough to be seen under a hand lens. Colours vary from yellowish green when the gall first appears in May, through red and purple, to brown on reaching maturity in August.

Colonization is sometimes so dense as to cause considerable damage to infected trees.

Closely related mites produce similar galls on other rosaceous plants, such as hawthorns (*Crataegus* spp.), mountain ash (*Sorbus aucuparia*) and white beam (*S. aria*).

Pear

Fruit galled by dipteron, gall-midge **Lestodiplosis pyri** (=*Cecidomyia* **114** *nigra*, *C. pyricola*).

'Black pear.' The gall is initiated by a female which deposits several eggs in the expanding flower-bud. Upon hatching, the larvae feed on the tissues within the centrally placed ovary, the enveloping receptacle meanwhile swelling abnormally. When fully fed, in June–July, the insects make their way out of the gall between the remains of the floral parts, over-winter in the soil as pupae, and the imagines appear in the following spring. After the parasites have left, the galls turn black and usually fall from the tree.

The average diameter of a mature gall is 1·5 cm, and the usual number of larvae in each varies from two to five. A serious pest in some orchards and gardens.

Malus
Apple (*M. sylvestris*)
Branch galled by homopteran, aphid

115-20 Eriosoma lanigerum (= *Schizoneura lanigerum, Aphis lanigera, Eriosoma mali*).

'American blight' or 'woolly aphid'. The feeding aphids pierce the cambium, causing it to produce a spongy growth of thin-walled cells, and an affected branch becomes distorted with irregular, knotted swellings, which are first soft and later woody. Old growths sometimes become huge. The insects themselves are reddish brown, but are largely concealed by their copious secretion of waxy wool, beneath which they live gregariously. In Britain, reproduction is largely viviparous, a single female producing 30–40 offspring, and about ten generations appear during the year. Winged forms are exceptional and arise mainly in autumn. The floccose secretion readily becomes airborne and aphids caught up in it are sometimes dispersed over considerable distances in this manner. Any eggs produced may survive the winter in bark crevices.

Immense damage is caused to trees in orchards and gardens, and treatment by chemicals is rendered difficult by the woolly covering. The discovery in America of a hymenopteran parasite, *Aphelinus mali*, which attacks

the pest, has enabled this to be used as an effective biological control in some countries. When introduced into New Zealand, for example, it reduced the infestation enormously. In European conditions, however, *Aphelinus* does not readily become established.

The popular name 'American blight' is misleading, since there is no proof that the aphid reached Europe from the New World.

GROSSULARIACEAE, Currant family
Ribes
Black Currant (*R. nigrum*)
Bud galled by acarine, gall-mite
Eriophyes (= *Phytoptus*) **ribis.** **121**

'Big bud.' Probably the most familiar gall in the kitchen garden. The colonized buds are at the nodes or in the clusters at the tips of the twigs. They undergo simple enlargement without suppression of the leaf or flower rudiments enclosed within and swell before other buds have opened. Although leaves and inflorescences occasionally appear from infected buds, they never develop normally, and fruit seldom forms. Galls may be found throughout the year, old ones remaining on the bush as ruptured buds. They mature in May–June when, if opened, they can be seen to be filled with numerous mites. The average diameter of a mature gall is 1·25 cm. but there is considerable variation.

Widespread and abundant. A pest which first received publicity in Britain in 1869, and which is closely related to forms causing similar bud galls on birch (*Betula*) and hazel (*Corylus*)—see Pl. 121. Severe infestation can bring about the death of currant bushes. Eradication is difficult, the cutting and burning of affected plants being, at best, only a partial remedy.

The mite also serves as a vector for the virus causing 'Reversion', when the growths generally are distorted and the leaves take on a darker tone of green and are of a different shape from those on unaffected bushes.

Red Currant (*R. rubrum*) Leaf-blade galled by homopteran, aphid **Cryptomyzus ribis.**

2

In spring, the wingless fundatrix begins to feed on the underside of a young leaf. Here she produces numerous off-spring whose activities cause the development of reddish, blister-like patches on the upper surface above their feeding sites. The entire leaf-blade may become affected, and also a large proportion of the leaves on a bush.

Winged females appear during the summer which fly to such herbaceous Labiatae as white and red deadnettles (*Lamium album* and *L. purpureum*) and wood woundwort (*Stachys sylvatica*), where breeding continues. In autumn, both males and females arise. These return to the currant bushes, mate and produce the eggs which pass the winter there, and from which the wingless females emerge in spring.

An abundant species in many localities.

CORNACEAE, Dogwood family
Cornus

Dogwood (*C. sanguinea*) Leaf-blade galled by dipteron, gall-midge **Craneiobia corni.**

25

A pouch gall of somewhat bizarre appearance which, although only common locally, is worth the trouble of locating. It resembles an inverted bottle with a rounded base inserted in the leaf, the neck hanging from the lower surface and the base forming a shallow dome on the upper epidermis. The length is 0·8–1·0 cm, of which some seven-eighths project from the under-side. As it matures, colours change from greenish yellow, sometimes with pink stripes, to purple and russet.

The galls actually arise from the midrib or side veins, and each contains several larvae. Development takes place from July onwards, the galls reaching maturity in August–September. The species is sometimes fairly plentiful in particular localities where hedge-trimming has been neglected for several years.

ARALIACEAE, Ivy family
Hedera

'Parsley' or 'Holly' Ivy (*H. helix* var. *cristata*) Leaf-blade apparently galled by acar-ine, eriophyid mite.

126

The host is a mutant with crinkly, wavy-edged leaves, which is commonly grown indoors for ornament. The natural undulations in its foliage some-times become colonized by an erio-phyid, whose activities seem to in-crease the irregularities of the leaf margin, causing the existing rolled edge to thicken, to rise up in vertical folds in the angles between the leaf-lobes, and sometimes to form pouches on the flat part of the blade's upper surface with a corresponding aperture on the underside. Initially, the colon-ized areas are the same colour as the rest of the leaf: later a reddish tint develops, patches of the outer surface become thickly covered with small pustules, and whitish hairs form on both surfaces of such galls.

Dimensions are very variable. The average thickness of the marginal roll is about 0·1 cm and the height of a pouch above the blade about 0·6 cm.

This appears to be a cecidozoan whose galls enhance the attractiveness of the host. Evidently it is little known. European monographs record no mites from *Hedera*; and, though Kieffer (*Eriophyid mites of California*, 1952) gives two species, neither of these brings about the kind of deformity seen here. Little information is available about the seasonal history of this colonizer although the limited observations made by the writer suggest that, even under conditions of house cultivation, there is a marked rhythm, the acarines becoming numerous in August–September and disappearing during the winter months.

Until more precise observations are available, the relationship between the mite and the gall must be regarded as uncertain. It could be an indirect one, such as that of an inquiline in a gall caused by some other parasite.

UMBELLIFERAE, Umbellifer family
Pimpinella
Burnet Saxifrage (*P. saxifraga*)
Pastinaca
Wild Parsnip (*P. sativa*)
Daucus
Wild Carrot (*D. carota*)
Inflorescence galled by dipteron, gall-midge **Kiefferia**(= *Schizomyia*, *Asphon-*
127–9 *dylia*, *Cecidomyia*) **pimpinellae.**

A unilocular and unilarval gall which can infect the upper part of the inflorescence axis or the stalk of an individual flower, but which develops most typically within the ovary, which it converts into an enormously inflated, utricular structure with thick walls. Often many occur in a single inflorescence: each is about 0·5 cm in diameter, and its colour ranges from greenish yellow to purple and brown. Specimens may be found from August to November. Pupation takes place in the gall, generally in September, and the imago emerges in the following month. It is easily reared from infected flower-heads gathered in mid-autumn.

When mature, the gall is attractive in a delicate, rather inconspicuous, way and is easily overlooked.

POLYGONACEAE, Dock family
Polygonum
Amphibious Bistort (*P. amphibium*)
Persicaria (*P. persicaria*)
Leaf-blade galled by dipteron, gall-midge **Wachtiella** (= *Cecidomyia*, *Dasyneura*) **persicariae.** 13

Often very numerous on a plant and easily found. The leaf margins are rolled across the undersurface, develop a characteristic spongy texture and become four to five times thicker than the normal blade. They may be spirally or otherwise contorted. The colours are greenish yellow, orange or pink; and generally purple or red near the petiole which remains bright after the rest of the leaf has dried.

A multilarval gall in which the larvae pupate. It appears in early July and is usually mature by August–September.

URTICACEAE, Nettle family
Urtica
Stinging Nettle (*U. dioica*)
Leaf-blade galled by homopteran, psyllid **Trioza urticae.** 132

Feeding by the insects inhibits the expansion of the leaves which become thickened, and either curled or formed into small pockets of variable size. These modified structures are thickly coated with long stinging hairs. Only a few nymphs occur in each of the colonized hollows. In the early stages, the galls are identical in colour with the rest of the plant, but become dark brown after the insects have gone away.

From a distance, galled parts superficially look something like the 'curly greens' of the kitchen garden.

Development generally occurs from early June, maturity being reached in August–September. Apparently very local in its distribution.

Stinging Nettle

Stem, petiole, leaf-blade or inflorescence galled by dipteron, gall-midge **Dasyneura** (= *Perrisia*, *Cecidomyia*) **4 urticae.**

'Nettle gnat.' Colonization is predominantly of structures close to the growing apex. A gall exhibiting a wide range of form, the variety depending partly upon the particular organ infested. Galls near the blade centre generally have equal proportions on both surfaces, and those near the petiole tend to be large, irregular, to spread partly along the veins and to affect mainly the lower surface. On the petiole and catkins the galls may develop as small, round swellings. They are slightly glossy and vary considerably in colour, from yellowish green to red and brown, and are normally unilarval, although they may coalesce. The galls first show in May, mature throughout the autumn, when the larvae emerge and pupate in the ground, and the adult insects appear in the following spring.

Widely distributed, and sometimes so abundant locally that every plant in a large nettle-bed is galled.

ULMACEAE, Elm family
Ulmus

Wych Elm (*U. glabra*)
Leaf-blade galled by homopteran, aphid **Eriosoma ulmi** (= *Schizoneura* **135–6** *ulmi, Aphis foliorum*).

A distinctive gall, developing from June onwards, which consists of one-half of the blade becoming swollen and puckered and rolled across the midrib. Flocculent matter occurs with the aphids inside the roll. The colour passes from yellowish green, through pink, to grey.

Towards autumn, when the gall becomes mature, the flow of sap lessens so that some of the cells shrink and the structure unrolls sufficiently to permit the insects to escape. (A similar mechanism operates in the release of the aphid *Pemphigus spirothecae*, Pl. 218 which causes the spiral gall on the petiole of poplar.) The present species is heteroecious with red currant (*Ribes rubrum*) whereon it sucks juices from the roots without causing galls.

Very numerous on some trees and several species of elm are infested. Two common predators are the elm gall bug (*Anthocoris gallarum-ulmi*) and the larva of the syrphid (hover-fly) *Pipiza*.

English Elm (*U. procera*)
Leaf-blade galled by homopteran, aphid **Schizoneura lanuginosa.** **137**

The leaf becomes converted into a pouch of variable size, the outer surface mealy grey at first, later changing to an attractive red and purple, while becoming puckered but smoother in texture. Aphids are present in large numbers within the pouch. Generally it develops between June and August, although an infested leaf may remain attached to the tree throughout the winter.

Dipterons, particularly hover-flies (Syrphidae), are the dominant predators and parasites in aphid galls. Members of the genus *Pipiza* are common in the present one.

The gall is very numerous on some trees. Several species of *Ulmus* are colonized.

English Elm

Leaf-blade galled by homopteran, **138** aphid **Tetraneura ulmi** (= *Byrsocrypta ulmi*, *Aphis gallarum-ulmi*).

'Fig gall.' A smooth hemispherical, conical or urn-shaped gall, with one or two peduncles, which develops on the upper surface of the leaf from the midrib or a vein. The average height is about 1 cm, but, in general, the larger the leaf the larger the gall. There are rarely more than six on a single blade. In colour it tends to resemble the adjacent tissues, although it becomes suffused with red when it passes towards maturity in early autumn.

Flocculent matter occurs among the aphids in the interior. The gall splits open at one end, and the insects leave through the orifice.

Many thousands of fig galls may be seen on some trees, and the host-range covers several kinds of elm.

JUGLANDACEAE, Walnut family
Juglans

Walnut (*J. regia*)

Leaf-blade galled by acarine, gall-mite **139** **Eriophyes tristriatus typicus** (= *Phytoptus tristriatus*, *Erineum juglandis*, *E. juglandinum*, *Phyllerium juglandis*).

Although the gall is most noticeable as a shiny convex protuberance upon the upper surface, infestation is essentially of the underside. Here there is a broad

and shallow concavity lined by a felt of buff-coloured hairs, among which numerous mites are to be found. Generally, the first indication of colonization appears in June, and growth is complete by August–September. A large specimen measures about 1·2 × 1·0 cm.

A single leaf seldom carries more than 6 galls, which lie to the side of the midrib, between the lateral veins. There are only minor differences between the colours of the upper side of the leaf and of the convex surface of the gall.

The species appears to be local.

BETULACEAE, Birch family
Betula

Hairy Birch (*B. pubescens*)

Branch or trunk galled by fungus, ascomycete **Taphrina betulina** (= *Exoascus betulinus*). Figs. 7, 8.

'Witches-broom.' Growths of this type are the most conspicuous of the tree galls in many districts. *T. betulina* causes brooms on hairy birch and a closely allied species, *T. turgida*, similar galls on silver birch (*B. pendula*). Development follows the same lines in both.

Early growth shows as numerous buds, with a woody core at their base, crowded together on one side of the stem near the site of infestation. So long as the causer remains active, elongation of the buds tends to be retarded, and the basal swelling may continue to increase and the mass of buds come to envelop much of the stem circumference. (A good example of a gall in this condition is shown in Fig. 7.) As the activity of the causer diminishes, many of the buds grow out and eventually give rise to the thin branchlets massed into the familiar

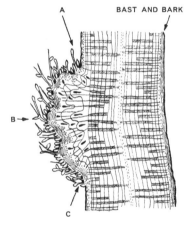

Fig. 7. Early phase of witches-broom (*Taphrina betulina*) on hairy birch.

Upper, external features ($\times \frac{1}{6}$).

Lower, internal features. Wood at A–B–C is proliferated under parasitic influence: note change in direction of grain, presence of radiating holes (black ovals) and abnormal thicknesses of bast and bark.

Fig. 8 Late phase of witches-broom (*Taphrina turgida*) on silver birch ($\times \frac{1}{80}$).

bunches which show up in silhouette from a distance on a host in winter aspect. The structures are persistent, coming into leaf each spring and increasing in size and complexity with time. Old brooms may expand to a metre or more and comprise 300–400 thin twigs. Colonization of a single host is sometimes dense: nearly a hundred witches-brooms have been counted on one tree about a century old.

Nesting house sparrows are common as successori ('casuals') in old galls of *T. turgida* along the main street of Bourton-on-the-Water, Glos.

Little is known about the mechanism by which proliferation of the host's tissues is brought about. Many fungi produce hetero-auxin (β indolyl-acetic acid) in laboratory cultures. This, or some other growth hormone synthesized locally by the parasite, might stimulate the kind of deformity seen here.

Fungi inducing witches-brooms belong to the three genera *Taphrina*, *Puccinia* and *Melampsorella*. At one time, broom galls on birch trees were believed to be induced by the mite *Eriophyes rudis* and large numbers of mites frequently occur as inquilines in the galls. Not all witches-brooms are the result of infestation by a parasite—mechanical injury caused by excessive browsing sometimes gives rise to massive growths of a similar kind, when the formations usually lack the compactness of the true galls (Pl. 4).

Silver Birch (*B. pendula*)
Leaf-blade galled by acarine, gall-mite
1 40 Eriophyes lionotus (= *Phytoptus lionotus, Cephaloneon betulinum, Phyllerium tortuosum, Erineum tortuosum*). Fig. 4 (b). A typical nodular gall, hemispherical on the upper and conical on the lower

surface of the blade. The interior is filled with dense hairs, among which the mites can be made out under a hand lens, and some of the hairs project as a reddish pubescence from the underside. The upper half of the gall is normally red-brown. Sizes are variable, but generally about 0.2×0.4 cm.

About six galls commonly occur on one leaf, forming in the nerve-axils. Although inconspicuous on first appearing in May, they become distinctly differentiated from the rest of the blade by the time they are fully grown in late August.

Alnus
Alder (*A. glutinosa*)
Leaf-blade galled by acarines, gall-mites *Eriophyes* spp.:
1. **E. axillare** (= *E. axillaris, E. nalepai, Erineum axillare, Phytoptus alni, Ph. alnicola*) Fig. 4 (a);
2. **E. brevitarsus typicus** (= *Phytoptus brevitarsus, Ph. purpureum, Phyllerium alnigenum, Erineum alneum*) ;
3. **E. laevis inangulis** (= *Phytoptus laevis, Cephaloneon pustulatum*).

Three kinds of gall-mite commonly infesting alder foliage are the following.

1. *E. axillare*. The species induces pouch galls which invariably develop in the angles between the midrib and the primary veins springing from it. Out-pocketings in the same position are a feature of several eriophyid galls on other plants (see *E. pulchellum* on hornbeam, Pl. 141). They occur either alternately or in pairs, extending from the petiole to within two or three veins of the leaf apex, and the regularity of their arrangement renders them conspicuous from a distance of several yards. Each gall consists of a convex reniform or oval swelling, 0.5×0.2 cm in size, which projects from the upper surface and changes in colour from green to

yellow, orange, purple and reddish brown. The interior is filled with russet hairs, among which the mites live. Some of the hairs project through to the underside and form more or less triangular patches in the axils of the veins which are considerably larger than the patches which normally occur in such positions on an alder leaf. Colonization may result in downward curvature of the midrib and considerable distortion of the blade.

Development begins in May and maturity is reached in August–September. Trees in a particular situation are frequently galled year after year.

2. *E. brevitarsus typicus.* An affected leaf develops concavo-convex blister-like swellings of very variable size, the domed part mainly on the upper surface. Occasionally a single pouch may invest nearly the entire leaf area. The outer surface of the pouch (i.e. that on the upper side of the leaf) is glossy, and the inner surface (underside) thickly coated with shining, tawny-coloured hairs. Inspection through a lens shows the extremity of each hair to be lobed. The mites live among the hairs.

Galls appear in June and reach full size in September–October, the upper side of the infected part of the leaf meanwhile changing in colour from pale green and light yellow to reddish brown.

3. *E. laevis inangulis.* Pimple-like galls, nearly always clustered on the upper surface, each of which is more or less spherical, firmly attached, glossy externally but hairy on the inside, and about 0·2 cm in diameter. The colour range is from green, through yellow and orange, to purple and reddish brown.

A single leaf may carry so many galls (up to 400 is not unusual) that its expansion is inhibited.

Reference has been made elsewhere (p. 29) to the apparent resistance to cold of some gall-mites. In central Europe, the writer has found all three of the alder eriophyids described above colonizing bushes distributed at high altitudes along the run-off from glaciers and within half a kilometre of the permanent summer snow-field.

Alder
Leaf-blade galled by dipteron, gall-midge **Dasyneura alni.** **148**

Oviposition results in the development of a roll gall particularly affecting the distal portion of the blade and extending along most of its margin. The edge curls upwards and the undersides of the veins become noticeably swollen. Initially green, the gall develops a russet tinge as it matures.

Development occurs from June to July onwards into the autumn. Plurilarval. A species which seems to be restricted in its range.

Alder
Grey Alder (*A. incana*)
Rootlets galled by fungal infestation, slime-fungus **Plasmodiophora** (= *Schinzia*) **alni,** or actinomycete **Actinomyces alni,** or bacterium **Rhizobium** (= *Bacillus*) **radicicola,** or a polymorphic species. **51** **53**

Considerable doubt exists as to the causative organism. The gall itself involves numerous thickened and shortened rootlets, clubbed together and forming a reddish or brownish mass of very variable size. It generally occurs on roots submerged in a stream.

Hard and firm when alive, but the parasite apparently dies and the rootlets separate after removal from water. A common gall found throughout the year, which appears to mature in mid-autumn.

CORYLACEAE, Hazel family
Carpinus

Hornbeam (*C. betulus*)
Branch or trunk galled by fungus, ascomycete **Taphrina** (=*Exoascus*) **carpini.** Figs. 9, 10.

'Witches-broom.' Almost any part of the stem may be affected and development is similar to the brooms on birch trees induced by *T. betulina* and *T. turgida*, but the twiggy bunches are usually stubbier, with branchlets which are thicker, shorter and fewer, so that the overall effect is less luxuriant. In fact, however, there is great variation in size, and brooms on the trunk sometimes became massive. The difference in formation between the twig and trunk galls is due to the slightly different habitat. When leaves appear in spring, these are stunted and soon fall off.

Growths are sometimes numerous on old trees, which continue to reproduce successfully despite heavy infestation. They also occur on hedgerow shrubs.

Locally common, especially so, perhaps, in parts of south-east England, but by no means generally distributed throughout the range of the host plant. No work has been carried out on the regional distribution.

Hornbeam
Leaf-blade galled by acarine, gall-mite
141 **Eriophyes pulchellum** (=*Phytoptus tenellus*). Fig. 4 (c).

The galls, which occur only on the upper surface of the leaf, are confined to the angles between the midrib and the main veins. Each takes the form of a smooth, shiny swelling, more or less triangular, and about 0·4 cm across the widest part, which attains full size in August–September.

Rather local in distribution: it is found principally on shrubs in hedgerows and woods.

Hornbeam
Midrib of leaf galled by dipteron, gall-midge **Zygobia carpini.**   **1**
The structure is typical of midge galls on petioles, midribs or leaf veins, being solid, spindle-shaped and extensive. The underside of the midrib becomes considerably swollen, each gall measuring about 3·0 × 0·4 cm, and the colour is generally paler than that of the leaf-blade. A single gall is unilarval, but several may occur together and coalesce, often causing marked distortion of the leaf itself.

Galls appear in June, mature in August–September, and persist until leaf-fall. Pupation takes place within the gall. Locally numerous on bushes in such situations as the more open parts of woodlands.

Corylus

Hazel (*C. avellanae*)
Leaf-bud, female flower-bud, or male catkin galled by acarine, gall-mite **Eriophyes avellanae** (=*Calycophthora* **1** *avellanae*, *Phytoptus avellanae*, *Ph. coryli*, *Ph. pseudogallarum*, *Acarus pseudogallarum*).

The bud gall resembles big bud on currants and consists of an aggregation of 20–40 scale-leaves, the inner ones thickened and hairy and often containing hundreds of mites. Their feeding activities wholly abort the young leaves or female floral parts enclosed within the scales.

Development is complete shortly before midsummer and the structure subsequently darkens to reddish brown. A migration occurs in early autumn, when the mites leave the old gall to colonize either a young bud or, more frequently, a newly formed male cat-

Fig. 9. Witches-broom (*Taphrina carpini*) on hornbeam. The tree is carrying over 200 small galls on its branches as well as several massive growths on its trunk, but it is still actively reproducing. (Height of tree, 40 ft.)

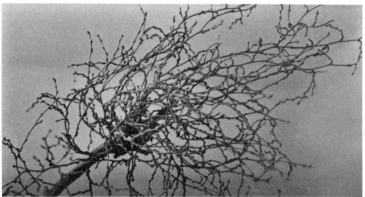

Fig. 10. Single broom of *Taphrina carpini* in winter aspect ($\times\frac{1}{6}$).

kin. They remain inactive between the catkin scales until the inflorescence starts to elongate in late winter. They then start feeding on the sap: the scales swell and separate widely and the anthers become distorted and eventually disappear. In April the mites quit the remains of the catkin and migrate to a bud.

Enemies of the causer are widespread and include a predatory midge, *Arthrocnodax coryligallarum*, and a chalcid parasite, *Tetrastichus eriophyes*. Another mite, *Eriophyes vermiformis*, which causes crinkling of the leaf on hazel, may also occur as an inquiline.

An extremely numerous species in many districts. If it is intended to rear the galls, these should be kept in a shaded place. Here, again, is a case of a gall-mite being able to withstand hard and prolonged frost, but being quickly destroyed by exposure to the direct rays of the sun.

FAGACEAE, Beech family
Fagus

Beech (*Fagus sylvatica*) including Copper Beech var.

Leaf-blade galled by acarines, gall-mites *Eriophyes* spp.:

1. **E. nervisequus** Fig. 4 (f);
150   2. **E. stenopis typicus** (=*E. stenaspis plicator, Legnon circumscriptum*);
151   3. **E. macrorhynchus ferruginus.**

Several eriophyids induce galls on beech leaves. Three examples are given here.

1. *E. nervisequus*. These filzgalls are rather inconspicuous, consisting of narrow ridges of felted hairs on the upper surface lying along the grooves of the lateral veins. The hairs are most noticeable in the early stages of devel-

opment when they are white: later they turn brownish and are then easily missed.

Specimens may be found throughout the period when the tree is in leaf. Common.

(Hairs also occur normally in the angles between the midrib and veins on the underside of the blade and these frequently become colonized by mites; but there is no growth response to the presence of the parasites and such hairy patches do not constitute galls.)

2. *E. stenopis typicus*. An interesting roll gall which consists of the entire length of the leaf margin becoming converted into a tube, about 0·1 cm thick with one to two windings, on the upper side. Nutritive hairs develop on the inner surface. Inquiline aphids may occur in the roll.

Glabrous and glossy, first pale green and ultimately brown, and present from May to October. Not as common in Britain as on the Continent.

3. *E. macrorhynchus ferruginus*. Shallow pouch galls of very variable form and size, which tend to lie between the major veins coming off the midrib. A characteristic feature is the development of club-shaped hairs in broad, shiny bands on the underside of the leaf. The overall colour is rust-red.

A particularly noticeable species in early summer. Locally common.

Beech

Leaf-blade galled by homopteran, aphid **Phyllaphis fagi.**   152

The aphids congregate on the underside of the leaf and their feeding activities cause the margins to become somewhat curved towards the undersurface and small swellings to develop on the upper surface in rows between the major veins extending from the midrib. An affected leaf eventually becomes discoloured and turns light brown. The insects secrete woolly fibres in which they are partly concealed, somewhat after the manner of the American blight aphid (*Eriosoma lanigerum*).

Infection becomes apparent about June and persists until August–September. Apparently patchily distributed, but locally common.

Beech

Leaf-blade galled by dipterons, gallmidges:

4   1. **Hartigiola annulipes** (= *Oligotrophus annulipes*, *H. piligera*, *Cecidomyia piligera*, *C. polymorpha*);

6   2. **Mikiola fagi** (= *Hormomyia fagi*, *Cecidomyia fagi*, *C. tornetalla*).

1. *Hartigiola annulipes*. A pouch gall which follows the insertion in spring of an egg through the epidermis of the upper surface, generally near the midrib. The structure develops wholly from the mesophyll, neither epidermis taking part in its formation. In July, a yellowish cylinder, thickly covered in delicate white hairs, erupts through the upper epidermis. By August–September, the gall is red-brown and mature; and it then develops a separation layer at its base, at which level it becomes detached from the leaf-blade to fall to the ground.

The size of a large specimen is about 0·5 × 0·3 cm. Unilocular and unilarval: the larva pupates in the gall after it has separated from the leaf, and the adult emerges in the following spring. A fairly common, widespread species. Occasionally, a single leaf may carry as many as 50 galls.

2. *Mikiola fagi*. These smooth, pointed, wax-coated pouch galls scattered about the upper surface, mostly near the midrib, yellowish green, red or purplish brown in colour, and 0·4 to 1·0 cm long, may be so numerous that nearly every leaf of the lower branches is galled. Although rarely found on the underside of the leaf, the positions of the galls are revealed here by small, hairy elevations. The chief features distinguishing them from *H. annulipes* are their larger size, the more pointed shape and the absence of hair on the main structure.

The life-history is similar to that of *annulipes*. The gall is unilocular and unilarval: it begins to grow in July; the larva pupates in the gall which becomes detached by a separation layer at its base and falls to the ground in autumn and the imago escapes in spring. The wax covering and the hard, sclerotic nature of its wall make the gall resistant to winter conditions.

Quercus

Pedunculate Oak (*Q. robur*)
Sessile Oak (*Q. petraea*)

Stem galled by homopteran, coccid
Asteriolecanium variolosum (= **157**
A. quercicola, *Coccus quercicola*, *C. variolosum*, *Asterodiaspis variolosus*, *A. quercicola*, *Planchonia quercicola*, *P. fimbriata*).

'Pit-gall.' A krebsgall which develops as a result of the feeding activities of the female coccid. As with coccids generally, the female is a sessile insect, remaining fixed for life in one spot on a young stem and sucking plant juices through stylets inserted into the cortex. This action arrests much of the tissue differentiation; but on the side where she is feeding, the outer layers undergo such localized development that she becomes surrounded by a wall of bark 1 mm high. An oval pit of approximately 3 × 2 mm is enclosed by the wall, and such pits may occur singly or in groups and generally contain feeding insects from May to October.

The coccid is one of the most exposed of all gall-causing animals, as she remains permanently on the host's surface without becoming enclosed within its tissues. (The American blight aphid on apple trees, is another externally situated causer, Pl. 115–20.)

Pit galls are plentiful in many districts, especially on scrub-oaks along roadsides.

Pedunculate Oak
Sessile Oak

Leaf-blade galled by dipterons, gall-midges, *Macrodiplosis* spp.:

158   1. **M. dryobia;**
159   2. **M. volvens.**

These are crescentic, marginal fold galls.

Folds caused by *M. dryobia* lie at the distal ends of the lateral veins and bend towards the underside: in *M. volvens*, the infolded edge is between the lateral veins and the curve is towards the upper surface. The pocket of the *volvens* fold tends to be somewhat broader than in the case of *dryobia*.

In both, the overlap is 0·2–0·4 cm, the colouring changes from green, through light brown to chocolate, and several larvae (about 4) occur together in a hollow which is devoid of hairs. Initially, the fold is tightly pressed against the blade, but when the larvae have ceased to feed, it gapes and allows them to fall to the ground, where they pupate.

Specimens may be found between June and September. Another gall-midge, *Clinodiplosis liebeli*, frequently occurs in both as an inquiline.

PEDUNCULATE OAK, SESSILE OAK

SELECTED EXAMPLES OF OAK CYNIPIDS (GALL-WASPS)

Where two galls occur in alternation, each is named after the generation which develops in it and not the generation which lays the egg leading to its formation.

In a book of this kind, it is impractical to cover all the cynipid species recorded as British: were this attempted, many of the basic facts would seem repetitive, the differences minor ones of interest to comparatively few specialists, and space would need to be provided by omitting material from other sections.

The 21 examples which follow comprise over one half of the oak cynipids known to occur regularly in Britain. Of the remainder, only 4 species can be accepted as both widespread and common: *Andricus albopunctatus* (SCHLECHTENDAL), *A. quadrilineatus* (HARTIG), *A. solitarius* (FONSCOLOMBE) and *Neuroterus aprilinus* (GIRAUD). The rest are all local or rare: *Andricus amenti* (GIRAUD), *A. callidoma* (HARTIG), *A. quercus-corticis* (LINNAEUS), *A. rhizomae* (HARTIG),

A. seminationis (GIRAUD), *Callirhytis erythrocephala* (GIRAUD), *Cynips agama* (HARTIG) and *Synergus clandestinus* (EADY).

Terminal or axillary bud galled by bisexual and rootlet by agamic generation of **Biorhiza pallida** (=*B. aptera, B. terminalis, Andricus terminalis, Cynips quercus-terminalis, C. aptera*). Fig. 1.

The familiar names, 'oak apple', 'apple gall', 'King Charles' apple', all refer to the bud gall. This follows from the insertion by a wingless female of numerous eggs in the base of a bud, which is almost severed from the twig in the process, and most of which is lifted off by the rapidly swelling gall in early May. When mature, in June–July, the oak apple is spongy in texture, often rose-pink, and 2·5–4·0 cm in diameter. Several may be clustered together. Plurilocular, averaging some 30 larval chambers.

In summer, adults escape through numerous exit-holes. There are two sexes which develop in separate oak apples (see pp. 22–3, alternation of generations—cynipids). It is rare for these individuals to be other than full-winged. In the male, the abdomen is narrower and more pointed at the tip than in the female. This is the generation to which the specific name *terminalis* is sometimes applied. After emergence, the blackened and shrunken remains of the gall persist through the winter.

Mating occurs in July, after which the females penetrate the soil and insert their eggs in tissues of the rootlets. Oviposition results in the development of the 'root gall', a spherical brownish object about 0·75 cm in diameter. Such galls occur singly or in groups and frequently coalesce: each is unilocular and unilarval and may become mature after some 16 months. The agamic

wasps which normally leave at the end of the second winter are wingless females (Fig. 13), to which the name *aptera* has been given. These climb up the trunk and lay the parthenogenetic eggs in the leaf buds which result in the development of oak apples.

Complex communities frequently develop. Several parasites and inquilines are known to occur among the oak apples and a few parasites even reach the subterranean galls.

A widespread species, the only one of the genus *Biorhiza* known in Britain, and a good one for the beginner in the technique of gall-rearing, as the bud gall is conspicuous, easily obtained in quantity, and lends itself readily to culture over dry sand in a jar. If collected at midsummer when mature (i.e. when suffused with a pinkish tinge), colonizers are likely to emerge in abundance.

Oak Apple Day, May 29, at a season when the bud galls are expanding and becoming colourful and attractive, commemorates the Restoration of the Monarchy, Charles II having returned to this country on May 26, 1660. It has nothing to do with the Boscobel incident, when he is said to have hidden from his enemies in the branches of an oak. This occurred during his wanderings as a fugitive after the Battle of Worcester, fought on September 3, when the galls had withered and turned black.

Terminal or axillary bud galled by **Andricus kollari** (=*Cynips kollari, C. lignicola, C. quercus-petioli, C. tinctoria, ? Andricus circulans*). **164–7**

'Marble gall', 'bullet gall', 'oak nut',

Fig. 11.   *Biorhiza pallida,* ♂ .

Fig. 12.   *Biorhiza pallida,* ♀.

(p. 151)

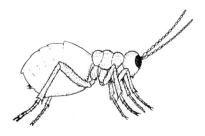

Fig. 13.   *Biorhiza pallida,* ☿ .
(p. 151)

Fig. 14.   *Andricus curvator,* ♀.

Fig. 15.   *Andricus curvator,* ☿ .

(p. 153)

EXAMPLES OF POLYMORPHISM

Fig. 16.   *Andricus quercus-radicis*, ♀.   Fig. 17.   *Andricus quercus-radicis*, ♂.

(p. 155)

Fig. 18.   *Cynips quercus-folii*, ♀.   Fig. 19.   *Cynips quercus-folii*, ♂.

(p. 156)

Fig. 20.   *Trigonaspis megaptera*, ♀.   Fig. 21.   *Trigonaspis megaptera*, ♂.

(p. 159)

FEMALES OF OAK CYNIPIDS (Not to Scale)

'Devonshire gall' (*not* 'oak apple'). Probably the most familiar of all insect galls to many people. A globular object, growing singly or in groups and sometimes coalescent, changing from pale green to warm brown both with age and illumination and becoming woody. Unilocular and unilarval. Size variable, parasitized galls frequently being stunted: the diameter of a non-parasitized example is about 2·5 cm. The galls mature in August, and causers leave in September–October, but specimens remain on the tree throughout the year. In confinement, large numbers of occupants other than causers emerge in May and June from galls collected in winter.

Plentiful on scrub-oaks in coppices and young plants in hedges, but scarcer on old trees. An introduced species, which reached this country about 1830 when galls were imported from the Middle East into Devon for dyeing West Country cloth or ink-making (the galls contain up to 17 per cent of tannic acid). Now widespread throughout Britain, and the subject of considerable Press controversy in the mid-nineteenth century when it was feared that the acorn crop would be ruined by its rapid spread and farmers deprived of useful fodder for pigs.

Observers who have reared this gall have invariably found all the emerging *Andricus kollari* to be agamic females, and it is uncertain whether the bisexual generation functions in Britain. As long ago as 1882, however, M. W. Beyerinck affirmed that the bisexual gall-wasp *Andricus circulans*, which causes galls resembling ant pupae in the axillary buds of Turkey oak (*Q. cerris*), is really the bisexual generation of *A. kollari*; an affirmation presented as a fact in the R.E.S. *Handbook*. The writer suggests further study of the breeding-cycle as a useful project for students.

Several parasites and inquilines are of common occurrence in marble galls, and old specimens often show the fine exit-holes made by some of these, which are generally smaller than the single circular aperture bitten out by the gall-causer herself. In some districts, the lesser spotted woodpecker (*Dendrocopus minor*) and other birds are predators. Many old galls bear numerous dark brown excrescences, which are due to the fungus *Phoma gallorum*.

For those of an experimental turn of mind who wish to try their hand at preparing ink from marble galls, a recipe is suggested here. Take one lb. of bruised galls, one gallon of boiling water, $5\frac{1}{2}$ oz of ferrous sulphate in solution, 3 oz of gum arabic previously dissolved, and a few drops of an antiseptic, such as carbolic acid. Macerate the galls for 24 hours, strain the infusion and add the other ingredients. For a few galls, measure out the components in proportion. In general, however, British galls have too little tannic acid for the best results—Aleppo galls have three times as much.

Like *A. kollari*, the next three cynipids supposedly alternate between British and Turkey oaks, but are known in this country mainly or exclusively by their agamic galls. In all, sexual fusion seems to be unnecessary for survival. The fourth has the roles reversed in that the bisexual gall is noticed far more frequently than the agamic.

Terminal or axillary bud galled by **Andricus corruptrix.** Fig. *b*, p. 32.

A small and inconspicuous gall, readily overlooked and probably commoner than at one time was believed to be the case. Basically a sphere, 3–5 mm in diameter, surmounted by two to five rounded lobes of varying size, the whole gall rough, scaly and flecked with red in spring but turning a smooth mahogany-brown in mid-autumn. Easily cut with a knife. The single agamic female appears in late July of her second year.

The bisexual generation is unknown in Britain. Dutch records show it to develop in pointed galls resembling those of *A. kollari* on *Q. cerris*.

Terminal or axillary bud galled by **Andricus lignicola** (=*A. lignicolus*). Fig. *c*, p. 32.

'Cola-nut gall.' The latest addition to the list of British oak cynipids. Kieffer J. J. (1910) recorded it from various continental regions stretching from Holland to Asia Minor. Although he stated that it was allegedly British, it has only been known here for certain since 1972, but it is apparently becoming widespread in S.E. England. There are records from localities as far apart as Hampshire, West Sussex and Epping Forest.

Often in small groups without coalescence. Each superficially resembles an undersized, misshapen gall of *A. kollari*, but is ovoid rather than spherical and rough and scaly instead of smooth. Dimensions up to 10 × 8 mm. Colour at first green, changing rapidly to grey-brown, with light red patches where the original bud-scales have separated. Hard and firm. The single agamic larva occupies a chamber near the base: the imago emerges in the July following the gall's inception.

Alternation in British material has only been observed under culture conditions. Galls of the bisexual generation are difficult to distinguish from those of *A. kollari* (Pl. 167). Margaret Hutchinson notes that agamic galls of *A. kollari*, *A. corruptrix* and *A. lignicola* may be found close together, even on the terminal part of the same twig.

Acorn galled by **Andricus quercuscalicis.** Fig. *a*, p. 32.

'Knopper gall'. A recent addition to the list of British cynipids. It was taken as agamic material in the early 1960s by Dr M. F. Claridge, since when something of a population explosion has occurred, invasion from the Continent evidently coming via the Channel Islands. As with *A. kollari*, Devonshire became the region where establishment developed, although the first arrivals of *A. quercus-calicis* were probably unassisted by human agency. Since 1971, the writer has been notified of the agamic galls on *Quercus robur* and, more doubtfully, on *Q. petraea*, in scattered localities extending from coastal parts of South Devon, through Gloucestershire, Northamptonshire and Huntingdonshire, to the King's Lynn area, a distribution suggesting orientation with wind.

The somewhat sticky, russet-green gall, 2 cm long, is hard, as is often the case with agamic galls in exposed situations. It is glabrous and shiny with knobby protuberances: the shape is that of a pyramid with an apical aperture and caved-in sides, and is distinctive. It results from distortion of the growing acorn. Infestation of a tree is frequently heavy.

A single agamic female is the only causer to emerge. Galls of the bisexual generation are known on the Continent, but there are no British records so far. They develop on catkins of *Q. cerris*.

Male catkin galled by bisexual generation of **Andricus quercus-ramuli** (=*A. autumnalis*). Fig. *d*, p. 32.

'Cotton gall' or 'woolly gall'. The alternating galls of this wasp contrast with those of the previous four cynipids which may, on occasions, colonize *Quercus cerris*: here only *Q. robur* (or *Q. petraea*) is used. The bisexual is the conspicuous gall: a flocculent, plurilocular mass, up to 3 cm across, looking much like a tuft of white cotton wool, usually on the staminate catkin but sometimes on a bud. The agamic gall has been recognized so seldom that few particulars are available. Apparently its form is that of an enlarged and elongated leaf bud.

Terminal or axillary bud galled by agamic and staminate catkin by **168–9** bisexual generation of **Andricus fecundator** (=*An. fecundatrix*, *An. pilosus*, *Aphilothrix fecundatrix*, *Cynips fecundatrix*).

Two galls arise, of which the larger and more familiar is the 'artichoke gall', 'larch-cone gall', 'hop gall' or 'hop strobile'. This is a unilocular, unilarval structure which forms as a result of oviposition of a fertilized egg in a bud. It is more plentiful on bushes than on large trees. A well-grown specimen is about 2·0 cm long, dark green or russet, and generally begins to develop in June, reaching full size during early autumn. It bears a superficial resemblance to a hop and has a swollen, solid core, in which the insect feeds, surrounded by overlapping bud scales.

The imago may leave the gall in the following spring or delay emergence for 2–3 years.

She is invariably a female, and utilizes the male flower-buds in which to deposit parthenogenetic ova, tending to select catkins of the pedunculate oak which come into flower some two weeks before those of the sessile oak. The resultant 'hairy catkin galls' are solitary in their manner of growth, and develop as oval, pointed, unilocular and unilarval bodies, 0·3 cm long, changing in colour from pale green to brown, and covered with whitish hairs. They are mature in May–June, and from them emerge the males and females to which the synonym *Andricus pilosus* is particularly applied. This is the generation which, after mating, gives rise to the fertilized eggs undergoing development in the artichoke galls.

Complex communities may become established in both galls. Apart from common parasites and inquilines, the gall-wasp *Andricus curvator* (Pl. 170–1) shows a preference for depositing its own eggs on buds already colonized by the present species, so that it may represent an early phase in the development of the inquiline mode of life.

Widespread and abundant in England.

Bud galled by agamic and leaf by bisexual generation of **Andricus cur-** **170** **vator** (=*An. collaris*, *An. perfoliatus*, *Cynips axillaris*, *C. curvator*, *C. tegmentorum*, *C. collaris*, *C. fasciata*, *Aphilothrix collaris*). Figs. 14, 15.

The life-cycle takes 2 years and can be regarded as commencing in midsummer, when the bisexual generation appears and gives rise to fertilized eggs. These are inserted in leaf-buds, and the insect shows a decided predilection for laying between the scales of buds already galled by the agamic generation of *Andricus fecundator* (artichoke galls). In any case, the resulting uni-larval 'collared-bud galls' are very inconspicuous, being 0·5 cm long and largely concealed by the bud scales until maturity, when the apex of a small, brownish core protrudes beyond the scales.

The 'collared bud' arises in July of the first year and persists until Feb-ruary or March of the third, when the female emerges whose unfertilized eggs cause 'curved-leaf galls' on the blade, midrib or petiole. These are pale green to light brown unilarval swellings, with an average length of about 0·8 cm, which are often plentiful on young shoots arising from the main trunk. Curved leaf galls develop rapidly in April–May, and the males and fe-males of the bisexual generation emerge in June.

Parasites and inquilines occur in both stages, and are particularly plenti-ful in the leaf galls. A widespread and abundant species, although the bud galls are difficult to recognize and locate.

Twig galled by agamic and leaf by -3 bisexual generation of **Andricus testaceipes** (= *An. sieboldi*, *Aphilo-thrix sieboldi*, *Cynips sieboldi*. *C. corticalis*).

The life-cycle lasts for 3 years.

Fluted 'red barnacle galls', in which the parthenogenetic females develop, colonize low-growing twigs, initially forming deep in the cortex and finally breaking through the surface as pyri-form swellings which push up the outer tissues like a cap. They commonly occur in rows near the roots of hedge-row bushes, where they may be cov-ered with leaf-litter. Each is about 0·6 cm high, at first red and soft and later brown and hard, and encloses a single larva.

Barnacle galls mature only in April of the third year when they become dehiscent. The females which emerge deposit unfertilized eggs and induce the formation of 'leaf-vein galls' on the petiole or underside of the midrib. These consist of oval, green swellings, about 0·5 cm long, maturing in August–September and containing larvae of the bisexual generation. After metamorphosis, this generation pro-duces fertilized eggs and gives rise to the barnacle galls.

Very common locally but incon-spicuous. The species may occur in almost any over-grown hedgerow.

Shoot tip galled by bisexual and lateral or terminal bud by agamic generation of **Andricus inflator** (*A. globuli*, **174–5** *Cynips inflator*, *C. globuli*).

The life-cycle is frequently protracted, sometimes occupying a span of 4 years.

The more conspicuous of the two galls is the 'twig gall', which is abun-dant in many districts on young oaks. It is unmistakable—a solitary, elon-gated swelling about 1·5 cm long, green or brown in colour, developed in the soft tissues of the new season's growth behind the shoot apex. The single larva feeds and pupates in a cylindrical chamber 0·3 × 1·0 cm in size, the galls develop from May onwards and mature in August.

This is the bisexual generation pro-ducing fertilized eggs which are inser-ted in buds. The resulting 'globular galls' occur on bushes and the small twigs of well-grown trees. Each is unilarval, spherical or oval, about 0·4 cm long, green, brown or bluish, and consists of a thick, sappy green rind enclosing a woody core in which the larva lies. The gall appears in September and matures in October, when the inner part separates from the rind and falls to the ground. Here it overwinters; and the adult which emerges in April of the second, third or even fourth year, is the agamic female which lays unfertilized eggs in the shoot tips.

Attempts to rear the agamic galls are rendered difficult by the unpredictable duration of the resting phase; but twig galls removed from the parent tree in spring frequently yield good results. Several parasites and inquilines are common.

Axillary bud galled by agamic and male catkin by bisexual generation of **176–7 Andricus nudus** (= *An. malpighii, Aphilothrix malpighii*).

The fertilized eggs giving rise to the female generation are laid in summer singly in buds within the leaf axils, causing spindle-shaped, slightly hairy 'Malpighi's galls', about 0·4 cm long. Each gall projects obliquely from a domed base, representing the aborted bud, and its distal end bears a short, peg-like process. The colour is greenish, often with reddish streaks. Growth takes place in about 3 weeks during autumn, after which it falls to the ground, and the winged imago escapes in early spring of the following year.

Parthenogenetic eggs laid by this generation in the developing male catkins high up the tree produce oval, unilarval 'bald-seed galls', about 0·2 cm long, which are particularly inconspicuous both on account of their size and position. These are yellowish or brown in colour, and up to seven

may colonize a single cluster of catkins. These are mature by May–June, and the males and females issuing from them produce the fertilized eggs which undergo development in the Malpighi's galls.

Both galls are small and require diligent searching. Perhaps rather rare as well as inconspicuous: There is reason for supposing that *Q. petraea* is preferred.

Root galled by agamic and stem by bisexual generation of **Andricus quercus-radicis** (= *An. radicis, An. trilineatus, Aphilothrix radicis, Cynips radicis*). Figs. 16, 17.

'Truffle galls' developing on upper parts of the root system at the base of the trunk are sessile, irregularly oval structures, some 4·0 × 6·0 cm in size, containing about 60 larval cells. Colouring ranges from cream, through pink and red, to russet. A young gall has the consistency of a potato, but later lignifies. Development begins in September of the first year; full size is reached in late summer of the second year, when the larvae pupate inside the gall; and the imagines emerge in the spring of the third year. These are females which deposit unfertilized eggs in the young shoots, thus inducing 'knot' galls in the succulent parts of first-year stems or, occasionally, in the petioles.

A 'knot gall' is about 0·1 × 0·2 cm large, unilarval, and develops in the stem cortex, above which the tissues become somewhat paler than the adjacent parts. Because of the natural irregularities in the epidermis of even a young stem, the gall is difficult to detect without peeling off the bark over a suspected swelling. It first shows in April, the bisexual generation appears in midsummer, and oviposition of their fertilized eggs results in the formation of the truffles.

Neither gall is easily located although, in fact, the species seems to be widespread and, in places, numerous. If gathered when mature, the galls are not particularly difficult to rear. Parasites and inquilines are frequent in both.

Leaf galled by agamic and bud by bisexual generations of **Cynips divisa** (= *Diplolepis divisa*, *Dryophanta divisa*, *Spathegaster verrucosa*).

The agamic generation feeds in the unilocular and unilarval 'red-pea gall', a glossy, somewhat flattened sphere arising from the underside of the midrib or a vein and attached by a short peduncle. Ten to fifteen, occasionally more, may occur on a single leaf. The average size is 0.5×0.6 cm: colouring passes from green, through yellow and orange, to red-brown: the season is from midsummer onwards.

Many of the agamic imagines emerge in October, although some galls opened at this time may be found still to contain larvae of the causer. After over-wintering, they reproduce parthenogenetically and their eggs develop in 'red-wart galls' formed in buds which become yellow, orange or russet structures, 0.4 cm long. Red wart galls appear in May, and the males and females of the bisexual generation escape in June and produce the fertilized eggs which undergo development in the red pea galls.

Inquilines and parasites commonly occur. The species seems to be abundant locally.

When attempting to rear the agamic generation, difficulty is sometimes experienced through the tendency of the red pea galls rapidly to harden in a dry atmosphere so that the imagines cannot perforate their exceptionally thick walls. It is advisable to gather infested sprays from among those on which some of the galls already exhibit escape-holes and either to insert the ends of the twigs in water or to keep the detached leaves in a jar containing an open tube of water.

Leaf-blade galled by agamic and bud by bisexual generation of **Cynips quercus-folii** (= *C. folii*, *C. scutellaris*, *Diplolepis quercus-folii*, *Dryophanta quercus-folii*, *Dr. taschenbergi*, *Spathegaster taschenbergi*, *S. giraudi*, *S. flosculi*). Figs. 18, 19. **182-5**

The spherical 'cherry galls' of the agamic generation are about 2 cm in diameter, smooth when mature, with a hard outer rind and spongy interior, often brightly coloured, and attached by a very short stalk to the underside of one of the larger leaf veins. Several may occur on one leaf. Each arises from a fertilized egg inserted in the phloem of the vein and contains a single larva which pupates in the gall during autumn. The females escape in December–February after the galls have fallen to the ground, first emerging from the pupae in October, but waiting inside the galls until weather conditions become favourable.

These females oviposit parthenogenetic eggs in dormant buds on small twigs, inducing the formation of 'violet-egg galls', about 0.3 cm long, unilocular and unilarval, which are dark red, purplish or nearly black in colour, with a velvet texture imparted by short white hairs. Although normally inconspicuous, they frequently show up well in strong illumination on bundles of twigs arising from old trunks. They grow in April–May, males and females make their escape in June and give rise to the fertilized eggs which undergo development in the cherry galls.

If collected when mature, both galls are fairly easy to rear, the unisexual particularly so. This can become the site of a complex community. At one time, the name *Dryophanta* was given to the unisexual and *Spathegaster* to the bisexual generation.

Dormant bud galled by bisexual and leaf-blade by agamic generation of

186–7 Cynips longiventris (=*Cynips substituta, Diplolepis longiventris, Dryophanta longiventris, Spathegaster similis*).

The 'green velvet bud gall' is an inconspicuous object, frequently hard to find, which forms in a dormant bud of the main stem or small twig, and is oval with a pointed apex, greyish green to golden brown in colour, bearing numerous white hairs and about 0·2 cm long. Unilocular and unilarval. Males and females emerge in May and their fertilized eggs are laid in the midrib or lateral veins on the underside of a leaf.

'Striped galls' form here, which are more or less globular, yellow or red, with whitish papillae frequently coalesced into blotches, stripes or concentric circles. Unilocular and unilarval: average length nearly 1·0 cm. Up to 8 galls may develop on a single leaf. The galls mature in November–December, when only females leave them and these are the insects which insert unfertilized eggs into the dormant buds, thus completing the life-cycle.

Evidently a somewhat local species. The striped galls are not difficult to rear if they are collected in autumn and kept in a cool place. Several parasites and inquilines are common.

Leaf galled by agamic and bud by bisexual generation of **Andricus ostreus** (=*Neuroterus schlechtendali, Andricus furunculus*).

Up to 0·3 cm across, the 'oyster gall' of the agamic generation usually lies between the midrib and lateral veins on the underside of the leaf, although occasionally it colonizes the upper surface. Apparently its colour is affected by exposure to the sun, and may be yellowish green, pink or brown, with small red spots. Unilocular and unilarval. Development begins in midsummer and proceeds rapidly: as it emerges from the vein, the gall is enveloped in leaf epidermis which splits to form two persistent valve-like flaps at the base. After the gall has fallen to the ground, the parthenogenetic female escapes in autumn of the same or following year.

This lays eggs in terminal or axillary buds, resulting in unilocular and unilarval 'April-bud galls', smooth, oval structures about 0·8 cm long, which grow so rapidly that less than a week elapses between the visible swelling of the bud and the emergence of the insect. This speed, the enclosure of the gall in the bud scales, and its greenish brown colouring, render it a particularly obscure structure, and it is easily missed. The single escape aperture in an old gall may be the only obvious sign of infestation. Males and females appear in May and produce fertilized eggs which develop inside the oyster galls.

Several parasites and inquilines infest each of the two phases. Widely distributed.

Leaf-blade galled by agamic and inflorescence or spring foliage by bisexual generation of **Neuroterus quercus-baccarum** ($=N.$ *baccarum*, *N. lenticularis*, *N. malpighii*, *Cynips lenticularis*, *C. quercus-baccarum*, *Spathegaster baccarum*, *S. varius*, *S. interruptor*).

Eighty to 100 'common spangle galls' often develop on the underside of a single leaf in July. These are flat, circular discs, about 0·6 cm in diameter and 0·2 cm thick, with a central elevation, slightly hairy, at first yellowish green and later reddish, and attached by a short stalk. Unilocular and unilarval. When mature (September), they become detached from the leaves and fall to the ground, when their undersurface can be seen to be whitish or yellow. The larvae continue to develop inside them after separation from the tree, and over-winter here, protected by the dead leaves which subsequently blanket the ground.

In April females emerge which lay parthenogenetic (unfertilized) eggs deep among the staminate catkins or young foliage. The resulting 'currant galls' are soft and spherical, about 0·4 cm in diameter, and change in colour from translucent green to pink and red. They closely resemble bunches of red currants. Unilocular and unilarval. Males and females of the bisexual generation emerge in June: after mating, the females pierce the lower epidermis of the leaves and deposit fertilized eggs. Each egg becomes enclosed in a spangle gall which erupts from the surface as a hemispherical growth and then expands laterally into a disc.

Both galls may become colonized by a variety of other organisms. Spangles lying on the ground are freely devoured by game-birds.

Formerly, the two galls were considered to be unrelated and separate generic names were applied, *Neuroterus* to the insects developing in the spangles and *Spathegaster* to those emerging from the currants.

Leaf-blade galled both by agamic and bisexual generations of **Neuroterus numismalis** ($=N.$ *reaumuri*, *N. vesicator*, *N. vesicatrix*, *Cynips numismalis*, *C. quercus-tiarae*, *Spathegaster vesicatrix*).

192–3
201–2

The form of the life-cycle resembles that of *Neuroterus quercus-baccarum*; but in the present species both generations colonize the same plant organ.

Gregarious 'silk-button spangle galls', which start to grow on the underside of the leaf in August, generally occur in very large numbers, and more than 1,200 have been counted on a single leaf. Each is unilocular and unilarval, and takes the form of a circular, golden brown disc, up to 0·3 cm across, with a central depression and raised margins, the whole tightly adpressed against the blade. A closeset covering of glossy hairs gives the impression of a silk-covered button. After falling from the tree, the spangles continue to swell by cell enlargement without division.

They over-winter on the ground, and the females which emerge in early spring lay parthenogenetic (unfertilized) ova in the expanding leaf-buds. Here, unilocular and unilarval 'blister galls' develop in the blades, each 0·3 cm in diameter, green or greyish in colour, and projecting as a convexity from both surfaces, with narrow ridges radiating from a papilla on the upper hemisphere. These galls mature in May–June, and the males and females arising from them produce fertilized eggs. Separate insertions of the ovipositor into the underside of the blade induce the formation of the crowded spangles.

As in the case of *Neuroterus quercus-baccarum*, the generic name *Neuroterus* was formerly given to the unisexual and *Spathegaster* to the bisexual generation. Both can be reared fairly easily from material placed over damp sand in jars kept in a cool place. Parasites and inquilines are frequent, particularly in the spangles.

Leaf galled both by agamic and **194-5** bisexual generations of **Neuroterus 203-4 tricolor** (= *N. fumipennis*, *Spathegaster tricolor*, *S. varius*).

Like the corresponding gall of *Neuroterus numismalis* (Pl. 192-3), the 'cupped spangle gall' of the agamic generation has the rim of the disc elevated to form a shallow cup: in the centre is a domed swelling. The average diameter is 0·3 cm and the colour greenish yellow, with a shiny coating of rose-red, stellate hairs. Although an immature specimen can be confused with the common spangle of *N. quercus-baccarum* (Pl. 190-1) · there are five features of distinction: (1) the upward curve of the rim is more pronounced; (2) the central elevation is less pronounced; (3) it is smaller (0·3 cm compared with 0·5 cm); (4) the underside is rarely buff-coloured; (5) generally, it is less numerous on a leaf. Colonization is of the undersurface of the blade, and the gall develops from July onwards.

After over-wintering in the spangle, the female lays parthenogenetic eggs which give rise to the bisexual generation developing in unilarval 'hairy-pea galls'. These are globular, downy, glistening structures, white, pale green or light yellow in colour which, when solitary, grow on the underside of the midrib or veins, but frequently coalesce, distorting entire clusters of leaves into aggregate masses. The average diameter is about 0·6 cm. They first show in May as small elevations of iridescent red or brownish hairs, which separate, elongate to 0·5 cm, and eventually fall off. The imagines emerge in June and produce the fertilized eggs which metamorphose inside the spangles.

Parasites and inquilines are common in both galls. A plentiful species in some districts.

Leaf galled both by agamic and bisexual generations of **Neuroterus albipes** (= *N. laeviusculus*, *Spathegaster albipes*).

The agamic generation develops in the 'smooth spangle gall', a structure about 0·4 cm across, variable in appearance but generally taking the form of a cream-coloured saucer with a diminutive cone in the centre. Gregarious, but less numerous on a leaf and more frequently on the upper surface than the other *Neuroterus* spangles. Growth takes place from July onwards, and it falls to the ground in October, whereupon it swells appreciably.

The female emerges in the following spring and lays unfertilized eggs, inducing 'Schenck's gall' on the margin of the leaf-blade or, more rarely, on the midrib. This is a solitary, rather inconspicuous oval body, about 0·1 × 0·2 cm in size, hairy at first and later smooth, its colour generally matching that of the undersurface. Its presence is typically betrayed by a near-by indentation in the leaf edge, since it inhibits the development of the leaf-blade beyond the point of attachment. (The agamic generation of *Andricus quadrilineatus* develops in an ovoid, longitudinally ridged gall which often arises in a similar indentation.)

Schenck's galls mature in May–June and give rise to the bisexual generation, the females laying the fertilized eggs which undergo development in the spangles. Both galls are unilocular and unilarval.

A common inquiline in the agamic gall is the dipteron *Clinodiplosis galliperda*. Widespread and locally common.

-9 Bud galled by bisexual and leaf-blade by agamic generation of **Trigonaspis megaptera** (= *T. renum, Cynips megaptera*). Figs. 20, 21.

The bisexual generation develops in leaf-buds on young oaks which, in spring, swell into 'pink-bud galls', reddish structures about 0·7 cm long and roughly spherical in shape. Emergence of the males and females takes place in May–June; and the fertilized eggs produced by this generation are inserted in the undersurfaces of leaves.

These give rise to the 'kidney galls' scattered about the underside close to veins, glossy, smooth, pedunculated bodies, passing from yellowish green to purplish brown, and about 0·2–0·3 cm in size. Each is unilocular and unilarval. Kidney galls develop rapidly during September, the peduncles shrivel in October, when the galls fall to the ground, and wingless females escape at the end of winter and lay parthenogenetic eggs in the unopened buds, thus inducing the pink bud galls.

The specific name *megaptera* was formerly given to the bisexual and *renum* to the agamic generation.

At least a dozen common parasites or inquilines may occur among specimens of the two gall-types, both of which are fairly easy to rear if kept in cool conditions. Regional distribution uncertain: locally common.

SALICACEAE, Willow family
Populus

White Poplar (*P. alba*) Stem galled by lepidopteran, moth **Gypsonoma** (= *Hedya, Spilonota*) **aceriana.**   **210**

A unilocular, unilarval gall, formed by the swelling of a young stem just behind the tip. Usually there is only a single gall on a twig, of much the same colour as an uninfested stem. The average length is about 2 cm. The caterpillar eats away the soft pith, and its droppings are excreted through a pore, below which they continue to adhere to the surface of the stem. Presence of the excreta is a useful indication that a gall is occupied. Growth takes place during June and July, the insect pupates in the gall, and the adult emerges in August.

After the causer has left, the stem may continue to elongate in the original direction without branching, but the gall cracks longitudinally, and an increasingly large cavity develops.

Aspen (*P. tremula*) Petiole galled by dipteron, gall-midge **Syndiplosis petioli.**   **213–4**

This dipterous gall should not be confused with those induced on the petiole by aphids of the genus *Pemphigus*, although it somewhat resembles the purse gall of *P. bursarius*. When fully developed, however, it tends to be pyriform instead of urn-shaped, and broadest towards the base of the blade; most of its long axis closely invests the petiole, thus eliminating the lop-sided development characteristic of the aphid pouch-gall; and the escape hole is circular and flush with the surface and quite different from the pouting, bird-like gape lined with white flocculent matter through which the winged aphids leave their host.

There are one or more larval compartments situated within the zone of vascular bundles. While the insect is growing, its larval cavity is connected to one of the vascular bundles, so that it may derive nourishment directly from this source as well as from the dividing and elongating cells of the cortex. Seldom more than 2 galls develop on a single petiole.

Maturity occurs in August.

Aspen

Leaf-blade galled by dipteron, gall-
212 midge **Harmandia globuli** (=*H. tremulae*).

In shape and colour, this gall somewhat resembles the egg of the puss-moth (*Cerura vinula*). It is a smooth, thimble-shaped structure, having a height and diameter of about 0·3 cm, which usually occurs in small numbers (up to 10) on a single leaf, where it develops on the upper surface of a major vein, with a corresponding recess on the underside. Unilocular and unilarval. The gall appears in June and soon becomes brightly coloured, changing from yellow to red and purple as it matures in August–September. The larva pupates in the soil.

Although widespread, the species is nowhere abundant.

Black Italian Poplar (*P.* × *canadensis* var. *serotina*)

Leaf-glands galled by acarine, gall-
211 mite **Eriophyes diversipunctatus.**

This variety of poplar has been introduced into Britain and is now widely planted, mainly in damp situations. At least some of the leaves of every twig bear two glands at the union between the blade and petiole. Infestation by the mites induces swelling, the transverse axis of the pair of glands sometimes reaching 1·0 cm, and the red colour may intensify.

Galls may be found from May until leaf-fall. Probably rather uncommon, although the structures are easily missed.

Lombardy Poplar (*P. nigra* var. *italica*)

Leaf-petiole galled by homopteran, aphid **Pemphigus bursarius** (= **21**▸ *Aphioides bursaria*, *Byrsocrypta bursaria*).

'Purse gall.' The gall is initiated in spring when a wingless female (fundatrix), hatching from an over-wintered egg, pierces the petiole of an unfolding leaf to suck the juices. At this point, the plant cells divide to enclose the insect in an urn-shaped, lop-sided pouch-gall, within which she reproduces asexually, and one end or flank of which is drawn out into a beak, often forked and powdered with white matter, through which her winged descendants escape. These (all females) migrate to such Compositae as lettuce (*Lactuca*) and sow-thistle (*Sonchus*), where they colonize the roots without causing galls and reproduce asexually. In autumn the aphids return to the poplars, and a generation arises consisting both of males and females, and these produce the fertilized eggs overwintering on the bark. Such alternation between two host plants is a common feature among aphids.

The gall is frequently the site of a complex animal community. Various

Diptera are generally the dominant predators in aphid galls, an important species in this case being the chamaemyid *Leucopis bursaria*.

When mature (August), the galls are often tinged reddish brown and spattered with honeydew and cast skins from the aphids. Rarely more than 2 galls develop on a single petiole. Approximate length, 1·5 cms. Abundant on Lombardy poplar throughout much of Britain—particularly on lower leaves—but less frequent on other *Populus* spp.

Lombardy Poplar

Leaf-petiole galled by homopteran,
8 aphid **Pemphigus spirothecae** (= *P. affinis*).

'Spiral gall.' A most remarkable gall of unique structure. As in *Pemphigus bursarius*, it is induced by a female which hatches from an over-wintered egg. Her feeding activities on the petiole result in its distortion into a ribbon-shaped spiral of two to three turns, the coils in tight contact but not actually fused. Here the causer is enclosed. After several moults, she produces up to 30 wingless daughters in June which, in turn, give rise to a second generation a month later. These moult, become winged and leave the gall in August, the twists of the spiral loosening sufficiently to permit their escape. Instead of migrating to another host, they deposit eggs on the poplar bark, from which males and females develop. After several moults, mating occurs, the females laying the fertilized eggs which over-winter.

The colours of the maturing gall pass from dark green, through red, to chocolate. Average length, about 1 cm. The interior frequently becomes a site for colonization by two saprophytic moulds, *Penicillium glaucum* and *Cladosporium herbarum*.

Pemphigus protospirae causes a larger spiral gall which matures earlier. When it opens (June–July), the winged offspring fly to the aquatic umbellifers *Sium latifolium* and *Berula erecta*.

White Poplar
Aspen
Black Poplar (*Populus nigra*)
Lombardy Poplar
Black Italian Poplar

Leaf-midrib (major vein) galled by homopterans, aphids *Pemphigus* spp.:

1. **P.** (= *Parathecabius*) **lysimachiae; 216**
2. **P. filaginis;**
3. **P. gairi;**
4. **P. phenax.**

Fundatrix galls which are sometimes confused with the petiole gall of *P. bursarius* as the life-histories are similar. That of *P. lysimachiae* typically lies away from the midrib: galls on the midrib proper may be caused by 2, 3 or 4. In these the summer brood leaves poplar to migrate, that of *P. filaginis* to various Compositae, of *P. gairi* to *Aethusa cynapium* and of *P. phenax* to *Daucus carota*. The three midrib galls are so similar that the best way to tell *P. filaginis* apart is by the colour of the nymphs in the gall, which are dark bluish green while those of the other two are pale yellowish green.

Lombardy Poplar

Leaf-blade galled by homopteran, aphid **Thecabius affinis.** 217

Pouch galls flecked with red, a frequent feature of poplar leaves, are induced by the first generation of this aphid.

White Poplar
Black Poplar
Lombardy Poplar

Leaf-blade, inflorescence or fruit galled by fungus, ascomycete **Ascomyces aureus** (=*Exoascus aureus, E. populi, Taphrina aurea, T. populina*).

219–21

'Gold leaf.' Colonization is generally of the leaf-blade. The gall takes the form of a pouch-like swelling, the convexity of which may be on either surface (although probably commoner on the upper side) with the concavity lined by fungal mycelium. The galls frequently coalesce and vary greatly in size, their usual length ranging from 1–4 cms. At maturity, the mycelium is golden and makes a striking impression when a tree with a high proportion of densely infested leaves is viewed from a distance.

Salix

Goat Willow (*S. caprea*)

Leaf-blade galled by dipteron, gall-midge **Iteomyia** (= *Oligotrophus*) **capreae.**

222

The galls are in the form of greenish pouches, up to 0·75 cm long, which frequently lie in rows between the main lateral veins. Each shows as a convex swelling on the upper surface with a reddish aperture on the underside.

Multilarval. The season is from June to September. It is common to find that the causer has oviposited in tissues already parasitized by the bean-gall sawfly (*Pontania proxima*), with the result that the present gall has developed superficially upon the first.

Goat Willow

Stem galled by coleopteran, longhorn beetle **Saperda populnea.**

223

'Timberman.' The largest of the British gall-causing beetles. The adult emerges from a gall in June–July. After mating, the female commences oviposition. She bites a hole through the bark of a branch or main stem and inserts a single ovum, moving 3–4 cm along the stem for each successive egg-laying. The larva feeds on the pith, eating galleries in both directions from the point where it hatched. Considerable swelling of the plant tissues develops around these galleries, and shows on the surface as a spindle-shaped gall about 2·5 cm long.

The hole through which the egg was inserted remains open, and ultimately forms a raised scar on aspen and a depression on willow. Pupation occurs in the second autumn and the adult beetle leaves the gall nearly 2 years after hatching. (A prolonged larval stage is a common feature of timber-feeding insects whose diet, presumably, is relatively low in nutritive value.) The emerging beetle generally bites an exit hole in the opposite side of the stem to the place of oviposition.

A local insect which is nowhere very plentiful. Its principal stronghold seems to be S.E. England.

Goat Willow

Leaf-blade galled by acarine, gall-mite **Eriophyes tetanothorax** (=*Cecidophyes tetanothorax, Phytoptus tetanothorax, P. salicis*).

22

The galls are more or less spherical, about 0·3 cm in diameter, slightly hairy, yellowish green, rose or red-brown in colour, and firmly attached. Up to 30 may develop on a single leaf, projecting from the upper surface while the mites enter and leave through an elliptical aperture on the underside. The interior is filled with hairs, some of which project through this opening.

Specimens can be found from June onwards.

The mite sometimes occurs as an inquiline in witches-broom galls on the same plant as well as in galls on other plants.

Locally common. Various *Salix* spp. are infested, but goat willow most frequently.

Common Osier (*S. viminalis*) Leaf margin galled by dipteron, gall-midge **Dasyneura** (= *Cecidomyia*, *Perrisia*) **marginemtorquens.**

The midge lays eggs in spring between the bud-scales. When the larvae hatch, they feed on the underside of one or both margins of a leaf rudiment, causing enlargement of the cells, with the result that the edge curls downwards and encloses the insects. Eventually, the infested margin rolls towards the midrib but rarely covers it.

A multilarval gall of very variable length (2–15 cms), slightly hairy, and of a somewhat puckered appearance owing to its blotches of green, yellow and red-brown colouring. After first showing in June, the structure matures in August–September, when the larvae fall to the soil to over-winter there as pupae. The imagines emerge in the early spring of the following year.

In some districts infestation is so dense that nearly every leaf of a plant is galled.

Another gall-midge, *Dasyneura* (= *Cecidomyia*) *clausilia*, causes smaller marginal folds which are unilarval and occur as separate rolls instead of being continuous. These also mature in autumn.

Goat Willow
Common Osier
Leaf-blade galled by hymenopteran, sawfly **Pontania viminalis** (= *P.*

pedunculi, *Nematus viminalis*, *N. pedunculi*, *N. bellus*).

A more or less oval gall up to 1·0 cm in length, bearing whitish hairs, generally greenish yellow in colour, and firmly attached to the underside of the leaf, usually on or near the midrib. There may be 6 (rarely more) on a single leaf. Their positions are marked on the upper surface by circular depressions, the raised margins of which are brown.

Unilarval. Development begins in June, the gall matures in July–August, the larva leaves before pupating, and the adult appears in the following spring.

White Willow (*S. alba*) Leaf-blade galled by acarine, gall-mite **Eriophyes marginatus.**

The only part of the blade to be affected is the margin, a small portion of which projects beyond the edge and then curls over upon the upper surface. Numerous mites live among delicate hairs lining the interior of the pocket. The gall is solitary, rarely coalescent, and there are seldom more than 10 on one leaf. Its texture is slightly pubescent. Initially the same colour as the rest of the blade, the tint passes through yellowish orange, red, purple and brown with increasing maturity. Galls first appear in June and mature in August–September, by which time each measures 0·3 × 0·1 cm.

Younger leaves near the end of a shoot tend to be infested more readily than older ones, and it is not uncommon to find colonization of terminal foliage already galled by the midge *Rhabdophaga rosaria* (camellia gall)—see Pl. 233–4.

A relatively inconspicuous structure, and evidently somewhat local.

This is one of the smallest of the roll galls produced on willows by mites. Other eriophyids roll the leaf margins of various species of *Salix*, often bringing about lateral curvature of an affected leaf so that it comes to resemble the blade of a scythe. Examples are shown in Pl. 228.

White Willow
Crack Willow (*S. fragilis*)
Almond Willow (*S. triandra*)

Leaf-blade galled by hymenopteran, sawfly **Pontania proxima** (= *P. capreae*, *P. gallicola*, *P. vallisnieri*, *Nematus gallicola*).

229–230

'Bean gall.' Several commonly occur on one leaf, projecting equally from both surfaces. Approximate size, 1·2 × 0·6 cm ·and 0·8 cm thick. Shades of colouring seem to depend to some extent on the species of *Salix* attacked: thus, unemerged galls on *S. triandra* tend to be red above and yellowish green below, while those on *S. fragilis* are generally reddish on both surfaces.

There are two broods, which may partly account for the remarkable abundance of bean galls in many places. Galls of the first brood, which develop after eggs are laid in leaf-buds in May, become full-grown in June–July, and those of the second mature in September–October. Each is unilarval and, although solid at first, becomes unilocular as the occupant eats out a central cavity. The fully fed grub pupates within a yellow cocoon on the bark or underground.

Two features are particularly noteworthy:

1. Gall formation is evidently induced by a substance injected by the female at the time of egg-laying, since galls are well advanced before hatching occurs, a gall may continue to grow after the egg is destroyed by a needle, and galls sometimes develop even if the insect merely pierces the leaf without actually laying.

2. This is one of the few hymenopteran causers which discharges its excreta from the gall while still a larva, the animal biting a hole in the floor through which the droppings escape.

Adults are mostly females which lay parthenogenetic ova, the males being rare. Two enemies are particularly common: an ichneumon-fly, *Angitia vestigialis*, which directly parasitizes the sawfly larva and kills it; and a small black weevil, *Balanobius salicivorus*. The latter deposits eggs in the young galls, and the sawfly grubs are destroyed in some way by the colonization. The weevil larva pupates in the soil.

Frequently the galls are heavily infested with the fungus *Melampsora*, even when this does not occur on other parts of the host plants in the locality.

Almond Willow
Common Osier

Male catkin and leaf-bud galled by dipteron, gall-midge **Rhabdophaga** (= *Cecidomyia*) **heterobia.**

22

There are two generations in the year. The first emerges in May from the catkin gall, a multilarval structure typically appears as a spherical or conical, downy mass, greyish white in colour, about 2 cm long, at the apex of the inflorescence. It seems to have the effect of prolonging the life of the catkin. Upon emergence, the adult midges deposit eggs in the leaf-buds, where typical rosette galls develop.

Both galls, but especially that on the inflorescence, frequently become thickly infested by the fungus *Melampsora*.

It is uncertain whether the fungal hyphae nourish the growing larvae, as happens in some other galls.

Locally a common species, with great numbers of galls sometimes developing on individual bushes.

> Crack Willow
> White Willow
> Purple Willow (*S. purpurea*)
> Goat Willow
> Eared Sallow (*S. aurita*)
> Grey Sallow (*S. cinerea*)

Terminal leaves galled by dipteron, gall-midge **Rhabdophaga rosaria** (=*Cecidomyia rosaria*, *C. cinerearum*).

'Camellia gall' or 'terminal rosette gall'. The structure consists of 30–60 leaves, shortened and crowded together. Its diameter varies with the plant species, generally being larger on *S. caprea* (8 cm) than on *S. alba* (3 cm). Development begins when the leaves expand in June. The gall matures in August–September while still green; later turning brown and remaining on the tree throughout the winter until pushed off by new growth in the following spring.

Each rosette contains a single pinkish-coloured larva which, unlike many gall-midges, pupates within the gall itself. A common inquiline is another gall-midge, *Perrisia iteophila*.

Widespread and locally common. A particularly attractive gall.

> White Willow
> Crack Willow
> Purple Willow

Leaf-blade galled by hymenopteran, sawfly **Pontania vesicator** (=*Nematus crassipes*, *N. helicinis*, *N. lugunensis*).

Unlike those of some other willow sawflies (e.g. *Pontania proxima*), this gall is relatively thin-walled and does not involve the deeper tissues of the leaf to the same extent, being constricted basally and inserted only by a small portion. It develops mainly on the lower surface. The general shape is an oval, about 2.0×1.5 cm, and the colour greenish yellow, often with a suffusion of pink. Growth starts in June and the gall is mature in July–August, when the larva escapes, drops off suspended on a thread, and pupates outside the gall in a silk-lined cocoon.

As with *P. proxima* and *Rhabdophaga heterobia* the gall is frequently the particular site of infestation by the fungus *Melampsora*. Apparently local in its distribution, but detailed information is lacking.

> Common Sallow (*S. atro-cinerea*)
> Eared Sallow
> Grey Sallow

Stem galled by dipteron, gall-midge **Rhabdophaga salicis** (=*Cecidomyia salicis*, *C. argyrosticta*, *C. de geeri*, *C. salicina*).

A typical stem gall, which takes the form of a smooth, glossy, spindle-shaped swelling of the younger sections of growth, and generally occurring singly on a twig. The colour is similar to adjacent parts of the stem. Dimensions are very variable, about 2.0 cm long being common. Plurilarval and plurilocular, with up to 30 insects in one gall, the insects occupying thin-walled larval chambers scattered about within the ring of vascular bundles where they feed on the pith.

The gall matures in October and the fully fed larvae move towards the outer tissues, where they pupate. A short length of the pupal skin projects from the exit hole when the imago leaves.

Apparently somewhat local.

Grey Sallow

Stem galled by dipteron, agromyzid

236 Agromyza schineri.

Oviposition in the new season's growth results in the development of unilocular and unilarval cushion-like galls, up to 1·5 cm long, in the side of the soft stem, which frequently alternate to produce a zig-zag or spiral effect. Occupied galls are generally greenish, with longitudinal wavy lines of a paler colour; but empty galls are persistent, so that specimens in some condition occur throughout the year. Growth is complete by September–October, when the larva pupates in the soil and subsequently gives rise to the imago in the spring of the following year.

Solitary galls may be found, but up to 15 in a single season's growth are common. Young bushes are colonized more frequently than well-grown trees.

ERICACEAE
Vaccinium

Red Whortleberry (*V. vitis-idaea*)

Shoot galled by fungi, basidiomycetes:

237   1 **Calyptospora** (= *Melampsorella*) **goeppertiana;**

238   2 **Exobasidium vaccinii.**

1. *Calyptospora.* Infestation is by the teleutospore generation which appears to have the remarkable effect of stimulating growth in height and the development of additional shoots on the host. The gall forms as a smooth, glossy, spindle-shaped swelling of the axis, up to 8·0 cm long and frequently standing conspicuously above the level of the adjacent parts of the plant. Its colour

changes from yellowish green, through red to brown. Expansion of the leaves in the galled part is retarded and they may fall off prematurely.

Teleutospores arise in the epidermal cells. Galls may be found on *Vaccinium* at all seasons. In their first year, the fungal hyphae ramify between the cortical cells and extract nourishment from them by haustoria ('suckers'). In the following spring, they extend into adjacent tissues. The aecidial generation of the same fungus develops in the seedlings of silver fir (*Abies alba*). Neither uredospores nor spermogonia have been identified.

2. *Exobasidium.* Galls caused by species of *Exobasidium* occur on several plants of this family, including *Rhododendron* (e.g. *E. vaccinii* and *E. rhododendri*). Nearly every gall develops on the underside of the leaf-blade, with little indication on the upper surface of its position, and attains dimensions which are relatively enormous due to increase in the ordinary parenchyma cells of the leaf. It is typically an oval or globose outgrowth, more or less succulent, and almost completely sessile. At first smooth, the surface becomes powdery as the fungal fungus erupts through the surface and gives rise to basidiospores.

Exobasidium can colonize various structures on the aerial parts of its hosts. Galls on whortleberry branches are generally spindle-shaped and very variable in size. As they mature, they tend to become reddish.

OLEACEAE, Olive family
Forsythia

Forsythia (*F. suspensa*)

Shoot probably galled by bacterium, **Corynebacterium fascians.**

239
240

'Fasciation.' The structure is typical of

similar malformations in the stems of other vascular plants (Pl. 241–4). Besides *Forsythia*, those which seem particularly prone to fasciation include members of the oleaceous genus *Jasminum*, the malvaceous genus *Hibiscus*, spurges (*Euphorbia* spp.), plantains (*Plantago* spp.), holly (*Ilex aquifolium*), dogwood (*Cornus sanguinea*), rosaceous plants like *Cotoneaster horizontalis*, and various composites including dandelion (*Taraxacum officinale*), ploughman's spikenard (*Inula conyza*) and garden marigold (*Chrysanthemum coronarium*).

Fasciation in general is probably due to one of several causes: induction from without by such parasites as viruses, bacteria, fungi or mites, or spontaneous origin from within as a result of genetical changes. If parasitically induced, fasciation is a gall.

Whatever the cause, the usual modification is that of a broad, flattened, strap-like development of the main stem or branch, in which multiplication of the normal structures seems to have occurred with the individual units coming to resemble a bundle of sticks lying in juxtaposition side by side and fused together. The components are seldom strictly parallel, since there is a tendency for the fasciated part to splay out fanwise towards the growing tip, to become spatulate, and sometimes to curve or twist and to fork. Buds commonly develop on the affected parts: any leaves which expand are usually typical in outline but often undersized. Fasciation shows none of the complexities of a 'higher' gall. It might be argued that the localized concentration of organic material could be of nutritive value to a parasite.

The metabolic injury resulting from fasciation seems to vary with the species. It is sometimes associated with the accumulation of such pigments as anthocyanin (reddish) in the younger foliage and β–carotin (yellow) in the older, with loss of chlorophyll in both. These changes prevent photosynthesis and, if they become sufficiently widespread in a plant, are fatal.

When *Forsythia* is colonized by *Corynebacterium fascians*, other malformations may develop. Galls of very variable size in the form of clusters of swollen buds sometimes appear here and there, often on branches which are not noticeably fasciated. Such bud-clusters somewhat resemble the crown-gall tumours induced by *Agrobacterium tumefaciens* (Pl. 48).

Corynebacterium fascians apparently exists in certain soils and there seems good reason to suppose that the disease is aggravated by wet or water-logged ground. This being the case, it would be interesting to undertake projects involving the drainage of the soil around both colonized and uncolonized *Forsythia* shrubs to observe what happens. The only method of control known so far is that of cutting off and burning the infected branches. The disease is becoming increasingly prevalent in this country and, in places, seems to be reaching epidemic proportions.

Fraxinus

Common Ash (*F. excelsior*) Inflorescence galled by acarine, gall-mite **Eriophyes fraxinivorus** (= *Phytoptus fraxini*). **245–6**

An interesting gall, although lacking attractiveness both of colour and form. Typically, infestation results in swelling and fusion of the pedicels of individual flowers and often extends to the peduncle of the whole inflorescence. There is considerable distortion: a well-developed pedicel gall may be conspicuous from the ground as a brownish, lumpy mass, and attain a size of 2·0 × 1·5 cm.

When colonization is severe, practically every inflorescence on a tree becomes galled to some extent. Although reproductive capacity is reduced, seed continues to be set between the individual galls (see Pl. 246). Affected structures often remain attached to the host plant from one summer to the next, so that galls in some condition can be found throughout the year. The numbers of adult mites seem to reach a peak in September–October. Widespread and locally abundant.

It is common to find a tree infested by *E. fraxinivorus* showing signs of distortion in addition to those described above—particularly thickening and rolling of the blades of some of the leaflets or entire leaves. Among the various animals found in such galls are eriophyid mites, aphids, psyllids and midges. Their relationships need further study.

Common Ash
Leaflet galled by homopteran, psyllid
247–8 Psyllopsis fraxini.

A roll gall, infestation causing one or both margins of a leaflet to thicken and roll downwards and across until the midrib is reached. Colouring varies from yellow to red, purple and brown, and the dimensions are very variable. Galls are found from early summer onwards, generally reaching maturity in August–September when insects in all stages of development can be found within the roll, together with flocculent matter.

Common and widespread.

Common Ash
Midrib or rachis of leaflet galled by dipteron, gall-midge **Dasyneura** (*=Perrisia*) **fraxini.**   24
25

The gall shows as a greenish or russet pod-like swelling, on either side of the undersurface of the midrib or on the rachis. When mature, it opens on the upper surface by a longitudinal furrow, each margin of which can be seen to bear a row of minute teeth if examined under a hand-lens. Size variable, the long axis generally measuring 2·5–5·0 cm.

A single gall is divided internally into 4–8 unilarval cells. Growths appear in June and mature in September, when the larvae escape from the open cells and pupate in the soil. Another dipteron, the ash-midge (*Clinodiplosis botularia*) is frequently associated with this gall, and is probably an inquiline, although some earlier investigators believed it to be the actual causer.

Widely distributed, and commoner on young than on old trees.

SOLANACEAE, Nightshade family
Solanum

Potato (*S. tuberosum*)
Tuber galled by fungus, **Synchytrium endobioticum** (*=Chrysophlyctis endobiotica, Oedomyces leproides*).   54

'Black scab', 'black-wart disease', 'potato cancer'. The fungus over-winters in the soil as a small thick-walled, golden yellow sporangium. In spring this liberates swarms of motile zoospores which swim in the soil water and gain entry into the young tubers through the epidermal cells, particularly those of the 'eyes'. The galled parts soon develop as cauliflower-like swellings of variable size, at first warty and bright brown, and later turning black. The earliest symptom of black scab is the wrinkled and brownish appearance of the young sprouts. No hyphae are formed. The cells of the tuber adjacent to those attacked undergo rapid division, with the result that the gall becomes enormous, its size frequently exceeding that of the unaffected parts of the tuber. During the summer, spherical sporangia arise in the gall cells and these, too, give rise to swarms of zoospores which attack other healthy cells and infect new tubers. The over-wintering sporangia develop in the galls during the autumn.

The disease, which probably emanated from the Continent, was first noticed in England in 1901. Similar galls are caused on woody nightshade (*Solanum dulcamara*), black nightshade (*S. nigra*) and tomato (*Lycopersicum esculentum*). A related fungus, *Urophlyctis leproides*, galls the underground parts of white and red beet and mangel wurzel (*Beta maritima*), inducing the host to produce lobed cells which lengthen and penetrate between neighbouring cells.

Lycopersicum

Tomato (*L. esculentum*)
Root galled by nematode, eelworm
55 Heterodera sp. (including *H. marioni*).

Elongated, cylindrical or knot-like swellings of variable size arranged in rows on the roots of many plants are commonly caused by eelworms. Distinction between the various species requires the attention of a specialist and *H. marioni* is known to attack the roots of over 800 different plants. The life-history of gall-causing nematodes is typically as follows.

Immature eelworms pierce the tissues of a new host plant, sucking its juices and leading to gall formation at the site of injury. Growth is accompanied by moulting. At the end of the third moult, the female becomes a plump, pear-shaped sac containing up to 500 eggs, and then degenerates, her cuticle remaining as a cyst around the eggs. The juveniles develop inside the cyst, which remains viable for at least a year in dry soil, and eventually escape, sometimes living free for several months without feeding before colonizing a suitable host. The males do not become sac-like. They escape as the gall degenerates, and wander through the soil, seeking out and fertilizing the females.

SCROPHULARIACEAE, Figwort family
Veronica

Germander Speedwell (*V. chamaedrys*)
Leaf galled by acarine, gall-mite
Eriophyes (= *Phytoptus*) **anceps.**   **253**

Not unlike the dipterous gall on the same plant caused by *Jaapiella veronicae*, but distinguished from it by the fact that infested leaves are twisted instead of concavo-convex, and do not come together, meet and enclose smaller ones. The gall is hairy, very variable in size, and whitish, yellowish or brownish. It appears in June and matures in mid-autumn.

Locally common.

Germander Speedwell

251-2 Terminal leaves galled by dipteron, gall-midge **Jaapiella veronicae** (= *Perrisia veronicae, Cecidomyia veronicae, C. chamaedrys*).

A common and unmistakable gall, formed as a result of oviposition by the adult in a growing bud. Two terminal leaves, already partly expanded, are retarded in their further development, and their serrated margins unite closely, their undersurfaces outwards, to form a globular swelling. Growth is prevented of the small leaves enclosed within; and the outer leaves are often tinged red or purple and invariably carry a woolly pubescence, the hairs of which can be seen under a lens to be ribbon-like and jointed. The diameter of an average-size gall is about 0·75 cm.

Multilarval. Pupation takes place in the gall, and the emerging adults leave their empty pupal skins projecting among the hairs.

Galls are to be found in any month, since infestation can occur whenever buds put forth new foliage. Generally distributed and often abundant.

Veronica

Water Speedwell (*V. anagallis-aquatica*)

Brooklime (*V. beccabunga*)

Scrophularia

Figwort (*S. nodosa*)

Water Betony (*S. aquatica*)

Flower galled by coleopteran, weevil 254-6 **Gymnetron** sp.

Most of the gall-causing beetles are weevils (Curculionidae) and include members of the genus *Gymnetron* with 13 British species, some of which induce the formation of galls in flowers. Such a gall consists of little more than a swollen ovary, and may be so inconspicuous that its presence can only be detected by a careful comparison, side by side, of infested and uninfested blooms. For example, a flower of *Scrophularia nodosa* or *S. aquatica*, galled by ·*G. beccabungae*, is distinguishable from normal ones by the inflated appearance of the ovary; the fact that the brown corolla lobes lie flat on the top instead of projecting forwards as a hood, and tend to be particularly dark; and the persistence of the corolla itself, which frequently remains attached to the ovary after the ungalled flowers in the same inflorescence have gone to fruit and have lost the perianth. The gall of *G. villosulum* on *Veronica anagallis-aquatica* begins by having a thin wall and large cavity, but it is not noticeably different from a normal ovary. Later, the placenta and septa swell and the seeds fail to develop: by then the gall has become an oval of about 0·8 × 0·5 cm.

Galls generally occur from the onset of the flowering period and attain full size in July–August. In most species, each growth contains 1–3 larvae which pupate inside it. All appear to be local in distribution. If the galls can be detected, rearing them is straightforward.

Other Scrophulariaceae may be galled elsewhere than in the flowers. Thus, *G. linariae* (= *G. collinum*) causes spherical galls on the roots of toadflax (*Linaria vulgaris*), and *G. hispidum* elongated galls on the stems of several *Linaria* species. The genus is not wholly confined to Scrophulariaceae *G. pascuorum*, for example, occurs on ribwort (*Plantago lanceolata*).

Weevils of the genus *Gymnetron* should not be confused with those of

Cionus. In some districts, *C. scrophulariae*, among others, is common on figworts and mulleins, where it does not induce galls.

LABIATAE, Mint family
Thymus

Wild Thyme (*Th. serpyllum*) Terminal leaves galled by acarine, gall-mite **Eriophyes** (= *Phytoptus*) **thomasi.**

9

A filzgall which results in the terminal leaves of the shoots becoming clustered together in globular masses about 1·0 cm in diameter and thickly covered with long, white hairs among which the mites live. From a distance, the effect is that of white tufts of cotton-wool, or a mould.

Galls begin to develop in May and reach maturity in August–September. Inquiline mites are common. Apparently a widely distributed species throughout the range of the host plant.

Glechoma

Ground Ivy (*G. hederacea*) Leaf-blade galled by dipteron, gall-midge **Dasyneura glechomae** (= *Cecidomyia bursaria*).

260

'Lighthouse gall.' Colonization is invariably of the upper surface, where many galls may cluster together. Each is in the form of an erect cylinder with a rounded top, is somewhat hairy, and passes in colour from light green, through pink, to reddish brown. Height, 0·4 cm. Unilocular and unilarval. When mature, in August–September, it falls off, leaving a circular hole, and the insect pupates and over-winters in it.

Widespread and abundant. Easily reared indoors from infected plants which have been potted, or even from detached leaves kept in water.

Ground Ivy Stem, petiole or leaf-blade galled by hymenopteran, gall-wasp **Liposthenus latreillei** (= *Aylax glechomae,* *Diastrophus glechomae*).

261

One of the comparatively few gall-wasps colonizing herbaceous plants other than composites. The gall generally takes the form of a globular swelling, the size of a pea, involving most of the leaf-blade. If it develops on the petiole or stem, it may be elongated. Solitary or coalescent slightly downy, greenish at first and becoming red or purple as it matures. Unilarval, with the insect at the centre. The gall matures in August–September, when the larva pupates inside it to emerge the following May. During the winter, the gall becomes hard on the outside and fibrous within.

A widespread species which is common locally.

Ajuga

Bugle (*A. reptans*) Inflorescence galled by acarine, gall-mite **Eriophyes ajugae** (= *Phytoptus* *ajugae*).

262–3

The gall is a conglomerate structure of very variable size, involving the terminal leaves and the flowers in their axils. Affected structures become swollen and distorted and covered with a dense mass of whitish hairs. The leaves are generally streaked purple and red.

Specimens occur from June onwards, reaching maturity in August–September. Locally common in areas where colonization by the host plant is extensive.

PLANTAGINACEAE, Plantain family
Plantago

Ribwort Plantain (*P. lanceolata*) Leaf-blade galled by nematode, **Anguillulina dipsaci.**

264

The galls are simple swellings of the leaf-blade which arise separately between the veins and subsequently invest the veins themselves. There is loss of chlorophyll, development of cells (many of them multinucleate) which are larger than those of the normal mesophyll, and increases in intercellular spaces and mechanical tissue.

Galls occur throughout the summer months. The nematodes are numerous in each and escape into the soil when the infected leaves decay. A widespread species which gives rise to similar galls on nearly 300 plants.

Ribwort Plantain Inflorescence galled by lepidopteran, moth **Tortrix paleana** (= *T. icterana*).

265

A very variable gall. The most constant form of distortion is probably the swelling of the flower-spike. Typical additional signs which may be present include drooping of the apex, either forking of the spike or the development of 1–6 lateral extensions near its base, a darkening in colour, and a comparatively low seed-yield. Any of these can, however, be associated with other abnormalities, including fasciation and eelworm infestation.

Up to 6 larvae may occupy a single spike, and these pupate in the gall. When the imago is about to emerge, the pupa works its way towards the surface, so that some two-thirds of the empty chrysalis skin remains protruding between the undeveloped flowers.

Galls are present from May onwards and reach maturity around midsummer. The moths are readily bred out from infested spikes gathered when mature and stored in the dry in bags. Apparently a widespread species, although colonized heads are easily missed in tall grass.

CAMPANULACEAE, Bellflower family
Campanula

Creeping Campanula (*C. rapunculoides*)
Hairbell (*C. rotundifolia*)

Phyteuma

Round-headed Rampion (*Ph. tenerum*)

Flower galled by coleopteran, weevil **Miarus campanulae** (= *M. campanulata*).

2:

The gall is comparable with that of *Gymnetron* on Scrophulariaceae. Both causers are weevils (Curculionidae). The affected ovary swells considerably, with the placenta turning thick and fleshy, the ovules becoming aborted and the corolla failing to open and remaining greenish at the base. Frequently the gall develops asymmetrically, with one side apparently normal but for its lack of fertile ovules. In spite of these changes, a galled ovary is not particularly noticeable.

The dark larvae generally occur singly or in twos in each capsule and pupate within the gall. Not all weevils which induce galls on shoots are restricted to flowers. Thus, *Apion frumentarium* causes red swellings in the petiole and leaf-blade of sheep's sorrel (*Rumex acetosella*).

RUBIACEAE, Bedstraw family
Galium

Ladies' Bedstraw (*G. verum*) Shoot galled by dipteron, gall-midge

Geocrypta galii (=*Cecidomyia galii, C. molluginis*).

Galls generally occur in groups, forming a succession of cove-rings up to 2·5 cm in circumference, encircling the stem near the bases of the leaf-whorls. Four to five spherical, unilarval swellings are usual in a ring, each larval cavity opening to the exterior by a minute ostiole guarded by hairs: externally the colour is greenish when immature and deepens to red-brown in the later stages. The epidermis bears short, shiny hairs.

Development begins in May, and the galls reach full size in July–August, when the larvae escape and pupate in the ground. Apparently local in its distribution.

The gall-midge *Dasyneura galiicola* induces terminal galls which superficially resemble those of *Oligotrophus juniperinus* on juniper (Pl. 31). Generally, the imbricated leaves are reddish.

Hedge Bedstraw (*G. mollugo*)
Goosegrass (*G. aparine*)

Leaves galled by acarine, gall-mite
68 Eriophyes (=*Cecidophyes, Phytoptus*) **galii.**

An unmistakable gall, colonization resulting in the narrow leaves becoming rolled and more or less sickle-shaped, with the development of dense hairs within the roll. Initially, the galls form in May when, under a lens, the small mites can be seen to be torpid: as the summer progresses, they become increasingly numerous and active. Meanwhile the colour of the affected leaves passes from pale green to light brown. There is considerable variation in size: a large gall is about 3 cm long.

Although widely distributed, it is common only in restricted areas, is sometimes hard to locate, and tends to fluctuate considerably in abundance from year to year.

CAPRIFOLIACEAE, Honeysuckle family
Lonicera

Honeysuckle (*L. periclymenum*)
Inflorescence galled by homopteran, aphid **Hyadaphis foeniculi.** 270

The aphids feed on the base of each corolla, causing swelling, a stunted and deformed flower, and the development of numerous hairs. Severe infestation may result in the formation of a globular mass. Dimensions vary greatly, but the colouring is similar to that of an uninfested inflorescence. The season is mainly between June and August.

A particular feature of some localities where wood or hedge-clearing has been neglected: otherwise uncommon.

Honeysuckle flowers are also galled by the many-plume moth (*Orneodes hexadactyla*), one of the microlepidoptera.

Viburnum

Wayfaring-tree (*V. lantana*)
Leaf-blade galled by acarine, gall-mite
Eriophyes viburni (=*Phytoptus viburni, Cephaloneon pubescens*). 269

A gregarious pouch gall usually scattered about indiscriminately on the upper surface, although an occasional leaf may be found with all the galls on the underside. Typically, colonization is dense on one side of the midrib and relatively sparse on the other. Sometimes it takes the form of two broad bands separated by the midrib, passing forwards from the petiole and uniting near the apex. Infested leaves tend to be those which are seldom exposed to strong sunlight.

The height and diameter of each pouch are about 0·3 cm. A dense covering of shining hairlets imparts a velvet-like appearance which is distinctive and attractive. Colours range from green, through pink, red and purple, to brown. Development commences in May, the galls mature in August and fall with the leaves.

Apparently of local occurrence throughout the restricted range of the host plant, which is most abundant on the calcareous soils of southern England.

DIPSACACEAE, Teasel family
Scabiosa

Small Scabious (*S. columbaria*)

Shoot galled by acarine, gall-mite

271 **Eriophyes** (= *Phytoptus*) **squalidus.**

A filzgall, which essentially takes the form of a conspicuous mass of silky, long white hairs, among which the mites live. The various structures of the shoot are affected in different ways. Thus, the bracts on the receptacle elongate and swell while the flower itself is aborted and the flower-stalk truncated: the leaf segments are dwarfed and swollen instead of expanding: if the entire shoot is infested, the whole forms a diminutive, pubescent mass. At a casual glance, the infestation appears to be due to a fungus.

It occurs between June and November, reaching maturity in early October. Locally common wherever the host plant is found.

COMPOSITAE, Daisy family
Senecio

Groundsel (*S. vulgaris*)
Oxford Ragwort (*S. squalidus*)

Stem, inflorescence stalk or leaf-blade

galled by fungus, basidiomycete **Puccinia terrieriana** (= *P. lagenophorae*).

A comparatively new arrival in Britain. The first collection was made by Dr Dennis at Dungeness, Kent, on 13 August 1961, and in the following year the rust was collected widely in Great Britain and Ireland. It is now very common every summer. The synonym, *P. lagenophorae*, is a native of Australia, where it occurs on several genera of Compositae.

Puccinia rusts on composites are widespread, and the distortions they induce may be more general than those illustrated. Thus, when *P. suaveolens* colonizes creeping thistle (*Cirsium arvense*), the entire host becomes one enormous gall.

Before *P. terrieriana* arrived, the most conspicuous rust on groundsel was probably *Coleosporium senecionis*. Its aecidial stage is found on the leaves of Scots pine (*Pinus sylvestris*) and Austrian pine (*P. nigra*) and its uredospore and teleutospore stages occur widely on various species of *Senecio*, including cultivated or escape plants of cinerarias (*S. cineraria*, etc.). Its uredo pustules bear a superficial resemblance to the aecidial tumefactions given here, each containing a central mass of dark-coloured sporogenous tissue surrounded by a raised whitish fringe (the ruptured epidermis). Dimensions of the galls vary considerably: those on a groundsel stem frequently attain a length of 1–2 cm.

Common Ragwort (*S. jacobaea*)
Marsh Ragwort (*S. aquaticus*)
Hoary Ragwort (*S. erucifolius*)
Groundsel

Inflorescence galled by dipteron, gall-midge **Contarinia** (= *Diplosis*) **jacobaeae.**

Infestation typically affects the capitulum in which the florets are inserted, and sometimes extends to the axil of the inflorescence stalk. As many as one quarter of the total number of flowerheads in a single large clump may be attacked.

Unilarval. The insect hollows out a cavity in the tissues of the capitulum, but leaves a very thin partition between the florets and itself. External signs include swelling of the base of the inflorescence, a tendency for it to become pyriform, and the accumulation of a wine-coloured pigment in the involucral bracts which together may become set in a partial twist. The florets in a galled head never fully expand, and in many cases they do not break through the enclosing bracts. A single gall may attain a diameter of 1·0 cm on groundsel and 1·5 cm on ragwort.

The first galls generally appear in June and most of them are mature by September. Pupation takes place in the soil.

Whether this is a case of one good species affecting several plant hosts, or of a polytypic species, or whether various races of host are involved, are problems which could only be elucidated by breeding experiments.

Achillea

Yarrow (*A. millefolium*)
Leaf galled by nematode, eelworm
76 **Anguillulina** (= *Tylenchus*) **millefolii.**

An example of a nematode species colonizing restricted aerial parts of a plant, in contrast to such forms as *Tylenchus devastatrix* which can infest the entire shoot.

Spindle-shaped swellings may develop on the rachis—which tends to become bent in consequence—and more globular swellings on the pinnae. Galls are glossy, separate or coalescent, and pass from green to brown. The eelworms are crowded within a large cavity in each gall, the wall of which contains many collapsed cells as well as cells with extensive air spaces between them.

Galls may be found from June onwards becoming fully developed in August–September. Probably somewhat local and uncommon, but inconspicuous.

Yarrow
Axillary bud galled by dipteron, gallmidge **Rhopalomyia millefolii** (= 277 *Hormomyia millefolii, Cecidomyia achillae*).

Galls are situated near ground-level, in the axils of the long, finely divided leaves. Up to 6 may occur together, but never coalesce. Each consists of an enlargement of the bases of the leaf sheaths of the bud, and takes the form of an oval swelling with a terminal ostiole (mouth), the aperture leading by a narrow cylindrical passage to the larval cavity. The ostiolar passage is covered by downwardly directed, interlacing, white hairs. As the gall matures, the ostiole becomes calyxlike in appearance, with a 4–5-toothed fringe curving outwards around the rim. A mature gall is 0·8 cm long, slightly pilose, greenish yellow, reddish or brown, and unilarval.

Growth takes place from June onwards, and galls reach full size in July–August, but specimens in some condition can generally be found throughout the year. Locally common, but obscurely sited.

Arctium

Great Burdock (*A. lappa*)
Wood Burdock (*A. vulgare*)
Seeding head galled by dipteron, fruit-fly **Tephritis** (= *Trypeta*) **barda-**
278 **nae.**

The gall is the seed itself, swollen and ultimately killed by the presence within it of several larvae. It becomes dark brown and about 0·7 cm long. A single head may contain up to 12 galls, but these do not affect its external appearance and can only be detected when the surrounding bracts are peeled off. The larvae pupate in the galls in July and the imagines emerge a month later.

The occupants are easily reared from material gathered as soon as the flowers have withered, and set up with the stalks in water and the fruiting-heads enclosed in a bag of fine-mesh nylon.

Apparently widespread but, from its concealed position, a species which tends to be missed.

Cirsium

Creeping Thistle (*C. arvense*)
Stem galled by dipteron, fruit-fly
280–1 **Euribia** (= *Urophora*, *Trypeta*) **cardui.**

A spherical or oval gall near the top of the stem, involving several internodes, and with stunted, deformed leaves usually arising from its surface. When young, the gall is soft on the outside: as it matures, it hardens from the centre and eventually becomes woody, its colour changing meanwhile from yellowish green to light brown. Size of long axis, about 2·5 cm.

Plurilocular, usually with four chambers, each containing a single larva which eats its way downwards and increases the diameter of its gallery as it descends. The structure begins to

grow in early July and matures in August–September, pupation taking place inside the gall.

An unmistakable and widely distributed feature of patches of thistles colonizing waste ground.

Centaurea

Greater Knapweed (*C. scabiosa*)
Lesser Knapweed (*C. nigra*)
Stem galled by hymenopteran, gall-wasp **Isocolus scabiosae** (= *Aylax* 2
centaureae, *Diastrophus scabiosae*).

'Knapweed gall-wasp.' The female oviposits through the epidermis below the growing region, inducing long or rounded swellings of variable size in the superficial tissues. A large gall may reach a length of about 7·0 cm. The colouring is that of the adjacent tissues. Multilarval. Eggs are laid in June, the gall reaches full size in August–September, and the imagines emerge in the following year.

Not uncommon, particularly in calcareous districts, but readily overlooked on account of the similar colouring of the galled and ungalled parts of the stem.

Isocolus fitchi, a scarce species, galls the base of the stem of *C. scabiosa*: *I. jaceae* and *I. rogenhoferi* are sometimes common in *Centaurea* fruits.

Greater Knapweed
Lesser Knapweed
Seeding head galled by dipteron, fruit-fly **Euribia** (= *Urophora*, *Trypeta*) 28
solstitialis.

Each gall involves a growing seed. The embryonal tissue becomes aborted as the gall develops into a swollen, oval mass of about 1·0 × 0·8 cm, the lower part smooth and the upper half surmounted by a tuft of branched and tubular grey hairs. It normally contains a single larva. Development begins in July and the gall has attained full size by October–November, after which the larva pupates inside it. The adult appears in the early summer of the following year.

An exceptionally widespread and abundant species, but owing to the total concealment of the affected seeds within the fruiting head, no sign of infestation is visible externally. One way of detecting the galls is to press the head between the fingers, when any that are present can be felt as hard, woody objects like tiny date-stones.

The flies are easily bred out from flower-heads gathered in autumn and kept through the winter in a fine-mesh bag suspended in a cool place, such as a shed. Emergence generally takes place in May or June.

Sonchus

Field Milk-thistle (*S. arvensis*)

Sow-thistle (*S. oleraceus*)

Leaf galled by dipteron, gall-midge **286 Cystiphora sonchi.**

Usually a gregarious gall, 20 or more sometimes occurring on one leaf. Each consists of a shallow, glossy pustule, more or less circular in outline, about 0·4 cm in diameter, rising on the upper surface to a cone 0·1 cm high and slightly concave on the underside. During development in June–July, a pale, narrow oval forms in the centre where the occupants feed, and this is surrounded by an areola which is generally dark purple in colour, with a reddish stain spreading beyond it. The light patch shows particularly clearly on the lower surface. At the same time,

the apex of the cone becomes rougher in texture.

There may be two larvae. These pupate in the gall and the imagines escape in autumn from the concave underside, leaving the white pupal skins projecting.

Locally common, and sometimes abundant. Members of the genus *Cystiphora* are confined to Compositae. *C. pilosellae* commonly colonizes leaves of hawkweeds (*Hieracium* spp.).

Hypochaeris

Cat's Ear (*H. radicata*)

Shoot galled by hymenopteran, gall-wasp **Phanacis** (= *Aylax*) **hypochaeridis.** 284

Colonization takes place within the pith of any part of the shoot usually of the main stem, but also of the flower-stalk or petiole. Proliferation is well advanced before the larvae hatch. It shows on the surface as an elongated, succulent, wrinkled, greenish swelling of very variable dimensions. The average length is about 1·5 cm, but occasional specimens are nearly ten times this size. Pleurilocular, containing up to 50 larval cavities. The gall is full-grown in August–September, and the larvae pupate within it and emerge as adults in spring.

Galls from which it is intended to rear the occupants should be gathered at the end of winter. Young, growing specimens soon shrivel if kept in dry air.

A species which is sometimes common in localities where the plant has remained undisturbed for several years. *Phanacis centaureae* is a widely distributed but local species which causes similar galls in the stems of *Centaurea* spp.

Hieracium
Hawkweed (*H.* spp., especially *H. umbellatum* and *H. perpropinquum*)
Shoot galled by hymenopteran, gallwasp **Aulacidea hieracii** (= *Aylax hieracii, Ay. sabaudi, Ay. graminis, Cynips hieracii*).

285

The gall follows the insertion by the female in spring of eggs into either the vegetative or reproductive axes of the shoot—most commonly into a bud at the tip. It takes the form of an oval or pyriform swelling, frequently asymmetrical, thickly covered in silky grey hairs, and often 2–3 cm long. It may involve the inflorescence. Pleurilocular, containing about 20 larval chambers in fleshy tissue around a central empty space. A growing specimen is sometimes tinged pink or red, and is then conspicuous, but a gall near the tip of the shoot tends to be concealed in the terminal foliage. After maturity, it becomes smooth and brown.

Growth is complete by August, the larvae over-winter in the gall, pupate there in spring, and the adult wasps emerge soon afterwards through separate circular holes. Colonizers are easily reared from material collected in late winter and kept in a cool situation. Parasites and inquilines are frequent.

A widely distributed species which is said also to infest herbaceous plants of other families, including toadflax (*Linaria*) and couch-grass (*Agropyron*).

Other species of *Aulacidea* which induce galls on Compositae include *A. pilosellae*, which galls the leaf midrib of mouse-ear hawkweed (*Hieracium pilosella*) and *A. tragopogonis* whose galls develop in the base of the stem of goat's-beard (*Tragopogon pratensis*).

JUNCACEAE, Rush family
Juncus
Soft Rush (*J. effusus*)
Jointed Rush (*J. articulatus*)
Inflorescence galled by homopteran, psyllid (jumping plant-louse) **Livia juncorum**

28▮

'Tassel gall.' An interesting rosette gall which, at first, appears as a developing inflorescence but ultimately becomes an imbricated tuft of 60–80 red or brown foliaceous outgrowths. Several such clusters may arise close together, each up to 8·0 cm long. Usually they appear low down, rarely attaining the height of the unaffected parts of the plant, so that they tend to be obscured by surrounding vegetation and to be overlooked. If a specimen is removed and held upside-down, it resembles a tassel.

Galls occur between June and October and seem to mature in August–September. A common predator is the dipteron *Lestodiplosis liviae*.

GRAMINEAE, Grass family
Phragmites
Common Reed (*Ph. communis*)
Inflorescence stalk galled by dipteron, chloropid **Lipara lucens** (= *Lasioptera arundinis*).

290▮

Closely related to the gout-fly (*Chlorops taeniopus*). There is a single larva in the axis of the inflorescence stalk, occupying a torpedo-shaped gall about 6·0 cm long, the presence of which inhibits growth beyond its position, so that the internodes fail to elongate and the successive layers of leaves become crowded together and envelop the larval chamber. By August, the galls are greenish yellow and fully developed. Later they turn brown, the insects over-winter in them, pupate in May, and the adults emerge in June, each working its way along the core of the successive layers of enclosing leaves until it reaches the outside. These oviposit immediately, so that galls occur throughout the year.

The galls frequently become the sites of complex communities. The causer itself is attacked by such hymenopteran parasites as chalcid wasps (*Pteromalus* spp.) and the braconid *Polemon liparae*. The *Polemon* larva develops inside that of *Lipara* and actually speeds up its metamorphosis, so that it pupates in autumn instead of spring and then dies as a result of being parasitized. Three kinds of tiny chloropid flies and two of gall gnats utilize the gall tissues as inquilines. Secondary galls may be induced on the main gall by some of these insects without affecting the development of the *Lipara* occupant itself. These secondary gall-causers have their own parasites.

After *Lipara* or its parasites and inquilines have emerged, other insects may move in and colonize the empty gall structures. In some districts, a small black solitary bee, *Prosopis pectoralis*, builds its nest, comprising a row of superimposed cells, in the spacious larval chamber. The larvae of this bee, in turn, are attacked by two parasites, an ichneumon of the genus *Gasteruption* and the ruby-tailed wasp (*Chrysis cyanea*).

Widespread in reed beds, although somewhat difficult to locate. Other species of *Lipara* cause smaller galls on reed.

Poa

Wood Blue-grass (*P. nemoralis*)
Stem galled by dipteron, gall-midge
287 **Poamyia** (= *Hormomyia*) **poae.**

The stem swells slightly, producing a vertical split in the enclosing sheath from which 100 or so adventitious roots emerge. These divide in a most curious manner, parting neatly into two groups like hair on a human head, one half passing to the right and the other to the left. They envelop the sheath, interlacing and forming an oval body about 0·8 cm long, which changes in colour from light green to brown. Generally the stem becomes bent at the position of the gall. Infestation begins in June and the growth matures in September–October.

Unilocular and unilarval. Pupation takes place in the gall. Widespread, but easily overlooked.

Triticum

Wheat (*T. aestivum* and *T. turgidum*)
Flower galled by nematode, eelworm
Tylenchus tritici (= *T. scandens*). **293**

'Corn cockle', 'purples', 'false ergot', 'peppercorn gall'. The gall arises when the floral parts are developing. No grain is set: instead, the ovary swells to about 0·5 cm and turns purple, brown or black. It contains 10,000–15,000 young worms in a dormant condition, which escape into the soil from a fallen gall after this has become wetted in a subsequent season. Their vitality is remarkable, as they can remain alive and dormant in the ground for some 20 years. On becoming active, the young worms move to healthy plants and live here for a time as ectoparasites between the stems and leaf-sheaths before penetrating the floral organs. Reproduction occurs in the inflorescence and results in gall-formation.

Spores of the fungus *Dilophospora*

alopecuri adhere to the young worms and are transmitted by them to the plants where they cause 'Twist' disease.

A troublesome pest in some districts.

Agropyron
Couch-grass (*A. repens*)
Hordeum
Barley (*H. distichon* and *H. vulgare*)

Inflorescence-stalk galled by dipteron, **292** chloropid **Chlorops taeniopus.**

'Gout-fly' or 'ribbon-footed corn-fly'. This small dipteron (0·4 cm) is so numerous in some districts that considerable damage to cereal crops results from its activities. Eggs are laid in June on the leaves, generally singly on the individual inflorescences, of spring barley or, occasionally, on couch-grass growing near to barley fields. Upon hatching, the larva moves down into the shoot, which becomes thickened and the leaves dwarfed and imbricated, with the result that a cigar-shaped gall of variable size is formed. If the ear is about to develop, the larva eats a groove down one side of it and the internode, and the ear fails to separate from its sheathing leaf.

The insect excavates a small cavity at the base of the inflorescence and pupates here. Flies of this brood appear in early autumn and oviposit between August and October, mainly on couch-grass, but sometimes on self-sown or winter cereals. Again, the inflorescence becomes galled and no panicle is formed. The imagines emerge early in the following summer. There is a general trend towards an alternation between different host plants in the two broods.

On sand-dunes, marram-grass (*Ammophila arenaria*) is sometimes galled by larvae of one of the *Eurytoma* chalcids, which induce similar shortening and imbrication of the leaves. The parasites live in the haulm and the adults emerge in June. Chalcids are among the few hymenopterans which gall monocotyledonous plants.

INDEX

English names, and scientific nomenclature with authors, of gall occupants and host plants.
Principal scientific names of causers adopted in this book, bold type; synonyms, italics; other
names, Roman.
Numbers of colour plates in bold; references to text pages in Roman.

Abies alba MILL. 114, 170
Abutilon MILL. 117
Acarus pseudogallarum VALLOT
  146
Acer campestre L. 124
  A. pseudoplatanus L. 125
Aceria macrochela heter-
  onyx (NAL.) 125
  A. macrochela typica (NAL.)
  124
  A. macrorhyncha cepha-
  lonea (NAL.) 125
  A. macrorhyncha typica (NAL.)
  125
Achillea millefolii L. 179
Actinomyces alni (PÉKLO)
  145
Adelges abietis (L.) **25–6,** 114
  A. gallarum-abietis HALD.
  114
Aecidium elatinum PERS. 114
Aethusa cynapium L. 165
Agrobacterium tumefaciens
  (E. F. SM. & TOWNS.)
  48, 14, 118
Agromyza schineri GIR. **236,**
  170
Agropyron repens (L.)
  BEAUV. 184
Ajuga reptans L. 175
Albugo spp. **44–6,** 120
  A. candida PERS. ex S. F.
  GRAY 18, 120
Alder 144, 145
Aleppo gall 154
Almond 135
Almond willow 168
Alnus glutinosa (L.) GAERTN.
  144
  A. incana (L.) MOENCH 145
Althaea L. 117
Ambrosia gall 128, 130
American blight **115–20,** 138,
  149, 150
Ammophila arenaria (L.)
  LINK 184
Amphibious bistort 140
Anbury 119
Andricus autumnalis (HARTIG)
  156
Andricus circulans MAYR **167,**
  151
  A. kollari HTG. 151, 154, 155
  A. corruptrix (SCHLECH.)
  32, 15 ×

A. curvator HTG. **170–1,**
  156
A. fecundator (HTG.) **168–**
  9, 156, 157
  A. fecundatrix MAYR 156
  A. furunculus (BEYER.) 160
  A. globuli (HTG.) 157
  A. hartigi MARSH. 130
  A. inflator HTG. **174–5,** 157
  A. kollari (HTG.) **164–7,**
  23, 151
  A. lignicola (HARTIG) **32,**
  15 ×
  A. lignicolus (HARTIG) **32,**
  15 ×
  A. malpighii (ADLER) 158
  A. nudus ADLER **176–7,**
  158
  A. ostreus (HTG.) **188–9,**
  160
  A. perfoliatus SCHENCK 156
  A. pilosus ADLER 156
  A. quadrilineatus (HTG.)
  163
  A. quercus-calicis
  (BURGS.) **32,** 15 ×
  A. quercus-radicis
  (FABR.) **178–9,** 158
  A. quercus-ramuli (L.) **32,**
  15 ×
  A. radicis MAYR 158
  A. sieboldi (HTG.) 157
  A. terminalis FABR. 151
  A. testaceipes HTG. **172–**
  3, 157
  A. trilineatus HTG. 158
Anemone nemorosa L. 116
Angitia vestigialis (RATZ.) 168
Anguillulina dipsaci
  (KÜHN) GER. v. BEN.
  264, 176
  A. millefolii (H. LÖW) **276,**
  179
Anthocoris gallarum-ulmi (DE
  GEER) 137, 141
'Ant-pupa' gall **167**
Aphelenchus fragariae
  (BAST.) 130
  A. olesistus longicollis
  RYTZ 130
Aphelinus mali (HALD.) 138
Aphilothrix collaris HTG. 156
  A. fecundatrix HTG. 156
  A. malpighii ADLER 158
  A. radicis FABR. 158

A. sieboldi HTG. 157
Aphioides bursaria ROND. 164
Aphis atriplicis L. 121
  A. foliorum DE GEER 141
  A. gallarum-ulmi DE GEER
  142
  A. lanigera HAUS. 138
Apion frumentarium
  (PAYK.) 176
Apple 115, 138
Apple gall 151
April-bud gall **189,** 160
Arabis caucasica WILLD. 119
Arctium lappa L. 180
  A. vulgare A. H. EVANS 180
Arthrocnodax coryligallarum
  TARG.-TOZ. 148
Artichoke gall—oak **168,** 156
  —yew **32–3,** 116
Ascomyces aureus MONT.
  & DESM. **219–21,** 166
  A. pruni FUCKEL 135
Ash-midge 172
Aspen 164, 165
Asphondylia genistae LEEUW.
  128
  A. mayri LIEBL. 128
  A. pimpinellae F. LÖW 140
  A. sarothamni H. LÖW
  85–6, 128
Asteriolecanium quercicola SIG.
  149
  A. variolosum RATZ. **157,**
  149
Asteriodiaspis quercicola,
  BOUCHÉ 149
  A. variolosus BOUCHÉ 149
Atriplex hastata L. 121
  A. patula L. 121
Aulacidea hieracii
  (BOUCHÉ) **285,** 182
  A. pilosellae (KIEF.) 182
  A. tragopogonis (THOM.)
  182
Austrian pine 178
Aylax spp.
  A. abbreviatus THOM. 131
  A. centaureae THOM. 181
  A. glechomae HTG. 175
  A. graminis CAM. 182
  A. hieracii SCHENCK 182
  A. hypochaeridis KIEF. 181
  A. minor HTG. **42,** 118
  A. papaveris (PERRIS) **41,**
  118

Aylax spp.—*cont.*
  A. potentillae MARSH. 131
  A. sabaudi HTG. 182
  A. splendens HTG. 131

Bacillus beyerinckii (H. & ST.)
  126
  B. radicicola (BEY.) 126, 145
  B. tumefaciens (E. F. SM. &
  TOWNS.) 118
Balanobius salicivorus (PAYK.)
  168
Bald-seed gall **177**, 158
Barbarea vulgaris R. BR. 120
Barberry 116
Barley 184
Bean gall **229–30**, 168
Bedeguar gall **99–102**, 132, 133
Bedstraw 136
Beech 148, 149
Berberis vulgaris L. 116
Berula erecta (HUDS.) COL.
  165
Beta maritima (L.) THELL.
  173
Betula pendula ROTH. 142,
  144
  B. pubescens EHRH. 142
Big bud **123–4**, 138
Biorhiza aptera FABR. 151
  B. pallida (OLIV.) **160–3**,
  23, 151
  B. terminalis MAYR 151
Bird-cherry 135, 136
Bird's-foot trefoil 129
Black currant 138
Black Italian poplar 164, 165
  nightshade 173
  pear **114,** 137
  poplar 165
  rust of wheat 116
  scab **54,** 171
Blackthorn 135
Black-wart disease 14, 172
Bladder bullace **104,** 135
Blennocampa pusilla HTG.
  96, 132
Blister gall **202**, 161
Blister rust 120
Box 126
Box-cabbage gall **78**, 126
Bracken 113
Bramble 130
Brassica napus L. 118
  B. oleracea L. 119
  B. rapa L. 119
Brooklime 174
Broom 128
Bugle 175
Bugle gall 121
Bullace 135
Bullet gall 151
Burnet rose 133
Burnet saxifrage 140
Bush vetch 129
Buxus sempervirens L. 126
Byrsocrypta bursaria (L.) 164
  B. ulmi L. 142

Calycophthora avellanae AMER.
  146
Cabbage 119, 120
Calyptospora goeppertiana
  KÜHN **237,** 170
Camellia gall **233–4,** 169
Campanula rapunculoides L.
  176
  C. rotundifolia L. 176
Capsella bursa-pastoris (L.)
  MEDIC. 120
Carpinus betulus L. 146
Cat's-ear 181
Cecidomyia achillae INCH. 179
  C. argyrosticta MACQ. 169
  C. barbarea CURT. 120
  C. bursaria BREMI. 175
  C. chamaedrys INCH. 174
  C. cinerearum F. LÖW 169
  C. clausilia BREMI 167
  C. crataegi WTZ. 137
  C. de geeri BREMI. 169
  C. excavans MACQ. 123
  C. fagi MOSLEY 149
  C. filicina KIEF. 113
  C. floricola RUDOW 123
  C. galii WTZ. 177
  C. heterobia F. LÖW 168
  C. limbivolens MACQ. 123
  C. loti MEIGEN 129
  C. marginemtorquens WTZ. 167
  C. molluginis F. LÖW 177
  C. nigra MEIGEN 137
  C. persicariae THEO. 140
  C. piligera MOSLEY 149
  C. pimpinellae F. LÖW 140
  C. polymorpha BREMI. 149
  C. pteridis MULLER 113
  C. pyricola NARDLI 137
  C. rosae MACQ. & BREMI.
  132
  C. rosaria F. LÖW 169
  C. rosarum HARDY 132
  C. salicina BOUCHÉ 169
  C. salicis SCHENCK 169
  C. sisymbrii SCHLECH. 120
  C. taxi INCH. 116
  C. tiliae SCHLECH. 123
  C. tornetalla BREMI. 149
  C. trifolii F. LÖW 128
  C. urticae PERRIS 141
  C. veronicae BREMI. 174
Cecidophyes galii NAL. 177
  C. tetanothorax NAL. 166
Centaurea nigra L. 180
  C. scabiosa L. 180
Cephaloneon betulinum BREMI.
  144
  C. myriadeum BREMI. 125
  C. pubescens BREMI. 177
  C. pustulatum BREMI. 144
  C. solitarium BREMI. 124
Cerastium L. 114
Ceratoneon extensum BREMI.
  121
  C. vulgare BREMI. 125
Cerura vinula L. 164
Ceuthorhynchus assimilis
  (PAYK.) 119

C. pleurostigma
  (MARSH.) **50,** 119
  C. sulcicollis PAYK. 119
Charlock, 119, 120
Chenopodium album L. 121,
  126
  C. urbicum L. 126
Chermes abietis L. 114
Cherry gall **182, 184–5,** 159
Chickweed 114
Chirosia parvicornis
  (ZETTER.) **21–2,** 113
Chlorops taeniopus
  MEIGEN **292,** 184
Chrysanthemum coronarium
  L. 167
  C. leucanthemum L. 128
Chrysis cyanea (L.) 183
Chrysophlyctis endobiotica
  SCHILB. 172
Cineraria 178
Cionus sp. **256**
Cionus scrophulariae (L.) 175
Cirsium arvense (L.) SCOP.
  180
Cladosporium herbarum
  LINK. ex FR. 165
Cleonus piger (SP.) 120
Clinodiplosis botularia
  (WTZ.) 172
  C. galliperda (F. LÖW) 163
  C. liebeli KIEF. 150
Clover 126
Club-root **49,** 119
Cluster-cup 115, 117
Cnaphalodes AMYOT &
  SERVILLE 114
Coccus quercicola BOUCHÉ 149
  C. variolosum RATZ. 149
Cola-nut gall 155
Coleosporium senecionis
  (PERS.) FR. 24, 178
Collared-bud gall **170,** 157
Common ash 171, 172
  hawthorn 115, 136, 137
  lime 121, 123, 124
  mallow 117
  maple 124, 125
  orache 121
  osier 167, 168
  ragwort 178
  reed 182
  sallow 169
  spangle gall **190–1, 198,** 161
  tormentil 131
  vetch 129
Contarinia jacobaeae (H.
  LÖW) **274–5,** 179
  C. loti (DE GEER) **87,**
  129
  C. tiliarum (KIEF.) **62–4,**
  123
Copper beech 148
Corn cockle 183
Cornus sanguinea L. 139, 171
Coronopus squamatus
  (FORSK.) ASCHERS 120
Corvus monedula VIEILL. 22
Coryllus avellana L. 146

Corynebacterium fascians
(TIL.) DOW. **239–40,** 170
Cotoneaster horizontalis DE-
CAISNE 171
Cotton gall 156
Couch-grass 184
Crack willow 168, 169
Craneiobia corni (GIR.) **125,**
139
Crataegus monogyna JACQ.
115, 136
C. oxycanthoides THUILL.
136
Creeping buttercup 116
campanula 176
cinquefoil 131
thistle 180
yellow-cress 120
Crowfoot-smut **40,** 116
Crown-gall **48,** 14, 118
Cryptomyzus ribis (L.) **122,**
139
Culinary pea 130
Cupped spangle gall **194–5, 203,**
162
Currant gall **199–200,** 161
Curved-leaf gall **171,** 157
Cynips aptera FABR. 151
C. axillaris HTG. 156
C. collaris HTG. 156
C. corticalis SCHENCK 157
C. curvator THOM. 156
C. divisa HTG. **180–1,** 159
C. fasciata SCHLECH. 156
C. fecundatrix HTG. 156
C. folii HTG. 159
C. globuli HTG. 157
C. hieracii BOUCHÉ 182
C. inflator THOM. 157
C. kollari HTG. 151
C. lenticularis OLIV. 161
C. lignicola HTG. 151
C. longiventris HTG. **186–
187,** 160
C. megaptera PANZ. 163
C. munismalis OLIV. 161
C. potentillae DE VILL. 131
C. quercus-baccarum MAYR
161
C. quercus-folii L. **182–5,**
159
C. quercus-petioli WEST. 151
C. quercus-terminalis FABR.
151
C. quercus-tiarae CURT. 161
C. radicis FABR. 158
C. rosae L. 133
C. scutellaris SCHENCK 159
C. sieboldi HTG. 157
C. substituta KINSEY 160
C. tegmentorum SCHLECH.
156
C. tinctoria SCHLECH. 151
Cystiphora pilosellae KIEF. 181
C. sonchi (F. LÖW) **286,**
181
Cystobus candidus LÉV. 120

Dandelion 177

Dasyneura alni (F. LÖW)
148, 145
D. clausilia (MEADE) 167
D. crataegi (WTZ.) **111–12,**
137
D. filicina (KIEF.) **20,** 113
D. fraxini (KIEF.) **249–50,**
172
D. galiicola (F. LÖW) 177
D. glechomae (KIEF.) **260,**
175
D. marginemtorquens
WTZ. **226,** 167
D. persicariae L. 140
D. sisymbrii SCHRANK
79, 120
D. thomasiana (KIEF.)
60–1, 123
D. tiliamvolvens RÜBS.
61, 123
D. trifolii (F. LÖW) **82–3,**
128, 132
D. ulmariae (BREMI.) **89,**
130
D. urticae (PERRIS) **133–
134,** 141
Daucus carota L. 140, 165
Dendrocopus minor (HART.)
154
Devonshire gall 154
Dewberry 130
Diastrophus glechomae
SCHENCK 175
D. rubi (BOUCHÉ) **93–4,**
130
D. scabiosae FÖRS. 180
Didymomyia reamuriana
(F. LÖW) **65–71,** 124
Dilophospora alopecuri (FR.)
183
Diplolepis bedeguaris GEOF. 133
D. divisa HTG. 159
D. eglanteriae HTG. **97,**
132
D. longiventris (HTG.) 160
D. mayri SCHLECH. 135
D. nervosus (CURT.) **98,**
132, 133
D. papaveris PERRIS 118
D. quercus-folii (L.) 159
D. rosae (L.) **99–102,** 23,
132, 133
D. rosarum GIR. 132
D. spinosissimae GIR.
132, 133
Diplosis jacobaeae LEEUW. 179
D. loti DE GEER 129
Dog rose 132, 133
Dogwood 139, 171
Douglas fir 114
Downy mildew 121
Dryophanta divisa HTG. 159
D. longiventris HTG. 160
D. quercus-folii L. 159
D. taschenbergi MAYR 159
Dryopteris filix-mas (L.)
SCHOTT 113
D. spinulosa WATT 113
Dyer's greenweed 128

Dysaphis ranunculi
(KALT.) **109–10,** 136

Eared sallow 169
Elm gall bug 137, 141
English elm 141, 142
Erineum alneum PERRIS 144
E. axillare SCHLECH. 144
E. clandestinum GERV. 136
E. juglandinum (PERRIS) 142
E. juglandis UNGER 142
E. oxyacanthae VALLOT 136
E. purpurascens GAERT. 124
E. tiliaceum (PERRIS) 121
E. tortuosum GERV. 144
Eriophyes ajugae NAL. **262–
263,** 175
E. anceps NAL. **253,** 173
E. avellanae NAL. **121,** 146
E. axillare CONN. **144–5,**
122, 144
E. axillaris CONN. 144
E. brevitarsus typicus
NAL. **146–7,** 144, 145
E. diversipunctatus NAL.
211, 164
E. fraxinovorus NAL. **245–
246,** 171
E. galii NAL. **268,** 121, 177
E. goniothorax typicus
NAL. **108,** 136
E. laevis inangulis NCL.
143, 144
E. leiosoma (NAL.) **59,**
121, 123
E. lionotus NAL. 144
E. macrochelus NAL. **72,**
124
**E. macrorhynchus aceri-
bus** NAL. **75–6,** 125
E. m. cephalodes NAL. **73,**
124, 125
E. m. ferruginus NAL. **151,**
148
E. marginatus CONN.
227, 167
E. megalonyx (NAL.) **74, 125**
E. nalepai FOCKEU 144
E. nervisequus (NAL.) **149,**
148
E. pini NAL. **27,** 115
E. pteridis NAL. 113
E. pulchellum SCHLECH.
141, 144, 146
E. pyri NAL. **113,** 137
E. ribis NAL. **123–4,** 138
E. rudis CANEST. 144
E. similis NAL. **103,** 135
E. squalidus NAL. **271,** 178
E. stenaspis plicator NAL. 148
E. stenopis typicus
(PGST.) NAL. **150,** 148
E. tetanothorax NAL. **225,**
166
E. tetrastichus NAL. **58,**
121, 123
E. thomasi NAL. **258–9,**
175

E. tiliae exilis NAL. **57,** 121, 122

E. t. leiosoma (PGST.) **121**

E. t. typicus (PGST.) **56,** 121

E. tristriatus typicus NAL. **139,** 142

E. vermiformis NAL. 148

E. viburni NAL. **269,** 177

Eriosoma lanigerum (HAUS.) **138,** 138, 149

E. mali (BING.) 138

E. ulmi (L.) **135–6,** 137, 141

Erysium cheiranthoides L. 120

Euphorbia L. 171

E. wulfenii HOPPE. **243**

Euribia cardui (L.) **280–1,** 180

E. solstitialis (L.) **282–3,** 180

Eurytoma ILLIGER 184

E. rosae NEES 133

Exoascus aureus FUCKEL 166

E. betulinus (FUCKEL) 142

E. carpini ROS. 146

E. deformans BERENDT 135

E. insititiae KERNER 135

E. populi (FUCKEL) 166

E. pruni DE BARY 135

Exobasidium rhododendri CRAM. 170

E. vaccinii (FOCKEU) **238,** 170

Fagus sylvatica L. 148

False ergot 183

Fasciation **239–44,** 170–1

Fat hen, 121, 126

Field milk-thistle 181

Field poppy 118

Field rose 132, 133

Fig gall **138,** 142

Figwort 174

Filipendula ulmaria (L.) MAXIM. 130

Finger-and-toe 119

Forsythia suspensa VAHL. 170

Fragaria vesca L. 130

Fraxinus excelsior L. 171

Galium aparine L. 177

G. mollugo L. 177

G. verum L. 176

Garden arabis 119

Garden marigold 171

Gasteruption LATR. 183

Gean 136

Genista tinctoria L. 128

Geocrypta galii H. LÖW **266–7,** 177

Gilletteella cooleyi (GILL.) 114

Glechoma hederacea L. 175

Globular gall **175,** 157

Goat's-beard 182

Goat willow 166, 167, 169

Gold leaf 166

Goosegrass 177

Gout-fly 184

Gracillaria syringella (FABR.) **2**

Great burdock 180

Greater knapweed 180

Green velvet bud gall **187,** 160

Grey alder 145

Grey sallow 169, 170

Ground ivy 175

Groundsel 178, 179

Grub 119

Gymnetron sp. **254–6,** 174

G. beccabungae (L.) 174

G. collinum (GYLL.) 174

G. hispidum BRULLÉ 174

G. linariae PAYK. 174

G. pascuorum (GYLL.) 174

G. villosulum GYLL. 174

Gymnosporangium spp. **28– 30,** 115

G. clavariaeforme (HEDW.) **29,** 115

G. juniperi LINK **30,** 115

G. sabinae DICKS 115

Gypsonoma aceriana DUP. **210,** 163

Habrocytus bedeguaris (THOM.) 133

H. periclisti CALLAN 133

Hairbell 176

Hairy birch 142

Hairy catkin gall **169,** 156

Hairy pea gall **204,** 162

Harmandia globuli (RÜBS.) **212,** 164

H. tremulae (WTZ.) 164

Hartigiola annulipes (HTG.) **153–4,** 149

H. piligera 149

Hastate orache 121

Hawkweed 180

Hayhurstia atriplicis (L.) **47,** 121

Hazel 138, 146

Hedera helix L. var. cristata 139

Hedge bedstraw 177

Hedge mustard 120

Hedya aceriana DUP. 163

Heterodera sp. **55,** 173

Heterodera marioni (CORNU) GOODEY 173

Hibiscus 171

Hieracium perpropinquum (ZAHN) DRUCE 182

H. pilosella L. 182

H. umbellatum L. 182

Hoary ragwort 178

Holly 125, 171

Hollyhock 117

Hollyhock rust **39,** 117

Holly ivy 139

Hololexis eglanteriae FÖRS. 132

Honeysuckle 177

Hop gall 156

Hop strobile 156

Hordeum distichon L. 184

H. vulgare L. 184

Hormomyia fagi HTG. 149

H. millefolii F. LÖW 179

H. poae 183

Hornbeam 146

House sparrow 22, 144

Hyadaphis foeniculi (PASS.) **270,** 177

Hypochaeris radicata L. 181

Ilex aquifolium L. 125, 171

Inula conyza DC. 171

Isocolus fitchi (KIEF.) 180

I. jaceae (SHENCK) 180

I. rogenhoferi WACHTL. 180

I. scabiosae (GIR.) **279,** 180

Iteomyia capreae WTZ. **222,** 166

Jaapiella genisticola (F. LÖW) **84,** 128

J. veronicae (VALLOT) **251–2,** 174

Jackdaw 22

Jasminum L. 171

Jointed rush 182

Juglans regia L. 142

Juncus articulatus L. 182

J. effusus L. 182

Juniper 115, 116

Juniper berry 116

Juniperus communis L. 115

Kidney gall **208,** 163

Kiefferia pimpinellae (F. LÖW) **127–9,** 140

King Charles' apple 151

Knapweed gall-wasp **279,** 180

Knopper gall 155

Knot gall **179,** 158

Lactuca L. 164

Ladies' bedstraw 176

Lamium album L. 139

L. purpureum L. 139

Larch 114

Larch-cone gall 156

Larix MILL. 114

Lasioptera argyrosticta MEIG. 130

L. arundinis SCHMID. 182

L. fusca VALLOT 130

L. picta MEIG. 130

L. rubi HEEGER **92,** 18, 130

Lavatera L. 117

Leaf-flower gall 127

Leaf-vein gall **173,** 157

Legnon circumscriptum BREMI. 148

L. crispum BREMI. 121

Lesser knapweed 180

Lesser-spotted woodpecker 154

Lestodiplosis liviae RÜBS. 148

L. pyri BARNES **114,** 137

Lettuce 164

Leucopis bursaria ROND. 165

Lighthouse gall **260,** 175

Lilac **2**

Linaria vulgaris MILL. 174
Lipara lucens MEIG. **290–1**,
128, 182
Liposthenus latreillei
(KIEF.) **261**, 175
Little black pudding 113
Livia juncorum (LATR.)
288–9, 182
Lombardy poplar 164, 165
Long-headed poppy 118
Lonicera periclymenum L. 177
Lotus corniculatus L. 129
Lupin 126
Lupinus nootkatensis DONN
ex SIMS 126
Lycopersicum esculentum
MILL. 173

Macrodiplosis dryobia F.
LÖW **158**, 150
M. volvens KIEF. **159**, 150
Male-fern 113
Malpighi's gall **176**, 158
Malus sylvestris MILL. 115,
138
Malva sylvestris L. 117
Mangel wurzel 173
Many-plume moth 177
Marble gall 151
Marram-grass 184
Marsh ragwort 178
Meadowsweet 130
Melampsora 168
Melampsorella goeppertiana
SCHRÖT. 170
M. caryophyllacearum
SCHRÖT. **23–4**, 114
Miarus campanulae (L.)
257, 176
M. campanulata 176
Midland hawthorn 136, 137
Mikiola fagi (HTG.) **155–6**,
149
Mock plum 135
Moss gall 133
Mountain ash 115, 137
Mouse-ear hawkweed 182
Myzus cerasi (FABR.) **107**,
136

Nail gall **56**, 121
Nectarine 135
Nematus bellus ZADDACH 167
N. crassipes THOM. 169
N. gallicola STEPH. 168
N. helicinis BRI. 169
N. lugunensis VALLOT 169
N. pedunculi CAM. 167
V. viminalis BRI. 167
Nepticula aurella (FABR.) **1**
Nettle gnat **133**, **134**, 141
Neuroterus albipes
(SCHENCK) **196–7**, **205–**
207, 162
N. baccarum MAYR 161
N. fumipennis HTG. 162
N. laeviusculus SCHENCK 162
N. lenticularis OLIV. 161
N. malpighii HTG. 161

N. numismalis (GEOF. in
FOURC.) **192–3**, **201–2**,
162
N. quercus-baccarum (L.)
190–1, **198–200**, 161, 162
N. reaumuri SCHENCK 161
N. schlechtendali MAYR 160
N. tricolor (HTG.) **194–5**,
203–4, 160
N. vesicator SCHLECH. 161
N. vesicatrix MAYR 161
Norway spruce 114

Oak apple **160–2**, 23, 151
Oak marble **164–6**
Oak nut 151
Oedomyces leproides SACC. 172
Oligosthenus stigma (FABR.)
133
Oligotrophus annulipes (HTG.)
149
O. capreae (KIEF.) 166
O. juniperinus (L.) **31**, 116,
128, 177
Orneodes hexadactyla (L.)
177
Orthopelma luteolator
(GRAVEN.) **134**
Ox-eye daisy 128
Oxford ragwort 178
Oyster gall **188**, 160

Papaver dubium L. 118
P. rhoeas L. 118
Parathecabius lysimachiae
(BÖRNER) 162
'Parsley' ivy 139
Passer domesticus (L.) 22
Pastinaca sativa L. 140
Peach 135
Peach-leaf curl **106**, 135
Pear 115, 137
Pear-leaf blister **113**, 137
Pear-leaf cluster-cup 115
Pedunculate oak 149–60
Pegomyia chenopodii
ROND. 126
Pekin willow **6**
Pemphigus affinis (KOCH) 165
P. bursarius (L.) KOCH
215, 23, 164, 165
P. filaginis (FONSC.) 165
P. gairi STROYAN 165
P. lysimachiae (BÖRNER)
216, 165
P. phenax BÖRNER &
BLUNCK 165
P. protospirae LICHTEN.
165
P. spirothecae (PASSER.)
217–18, 24, 141, 165
Penicillium glaucum LINK ex
FR. 165
Peppercorn gall 183
Periclistus brandtii (RATZ.)
133
Peridermium elatinum WALLR.
114

Peronospora parasitica
PERS. ex FR. **45**, 18, 121
Perrisia crataegi (WTZ.) 137
P. filicina KIEF. 113
P. fraxini KIEF. 172
P. genisticola (F. LÖW) 128
P. iteophila H. LÖW 169
P. marginemtorquens 167
P. tiliamvolvens RÜBS. 123
P. ulmariae (BREMI.) 130
P. urticae (PERRIS) 141
P. veronicae VALLOT 174
Persicaria 140
Phanacis centaureae
FORST. 181
P. hypochaeridis (KIEF.)
284, 181
Phoma gallorum (BRIARD)
166, 154
Phragmidium subcorticum
(LINK) 133
Phragmites communis TRIN.
182
Phyllanthous gall **80–1**, 127
Phyllaphis fagi (L.) **152**,
148
Phyllerium alnigenum KUNTZE
144
P. juglandis SCHLECH. 142
P. tiliaceum PERRIS 121
P. tortuosum (GERV.) 144
Phyteuma tenerum R.
SCHULZ 176
Phytomonas tumefaciens (E. F.
SM. & TOWNS.) 118
Phytomyza ilicis CURT. **77**,
125
Phytoptus ajugae NAL. 175
P. alni FOCKEU 144
P. alnicola CANES. 144
P. anceps NAL. 173
P. arianus CANES. 137
P. arionae CANES. 137
P. avellanae NAL. 146
P. brevitarsus NAL. 144
P. coryli PERRIS 146
P. fraxini KARP. 171
P. galii KARP. 177
P. goniothorax NAL. 136
P. laevis NAL. 144
P. lionotus NAL. 144
P. macrochelus NAL. 124
P. macrorhynchus NAL. 125
P. moniezi FOCKEU 124
P. myriadeum MURRAY 125
P. pseudogallarum TARG.-
TOZ. 146
P. purpureum DE CAN. 144
P. pyri MURRAY 137
P. ribis WEST. 138
P. salicis MURRAY 163
P. similis NAL. 135
P. squalidus NAL. 178
P. tenellus NAL. 146
P. tetanothorax NAL. 166
P. tetrastichus (NAL.) 121
P. thomasi NAL. 175
P. tristriatus NAL. 142
P. viburni NAL. 177

Picea abies (L.) KARST. 114
P. sitchensis (BONG.)
   CARR. 114
Pimpinella saxifraga L. 140
Pink-bud gall **209,** 163
Pinus nigra ARNOLD 178
P. sylvestris L. 115, 178
Pipiza FALLÉN 141, 142
Pisum sativum L. 130
Pit-gall **157, 158,** 149
Planchonia fimbriata FONSC.
   149
P. quercicola BOUCHÉ 149
Plantago L. 171
P. lanceolata L. 176,
Plasmodiophora alni
   MOLL. **51,** 145
   P. brassicae WORON. **49,**
   119
Ploughman's spikenard 171
Plum 135
Poamyia poae BOSC. **287,**
   183
Poa nemoralis L. 183
Pocket plum 135
Polemon liparae (GIR.) 183
Polycystis pompholygodes (LÉV.)
   116
Polygonum amphibium L. 140
P. persicaria L. 140
Pontania caprea (L.) 168
   P. gallicola (STEPH.) 168
   P. pedunculi (HTG.) 167
   P. proxima (LEPEL.) BEN.
   229–30, 13, 166, 168, 169
   P. vallisneri RATZ. 168
   P. vesicator BREMI. **232,**
   169
   P. viminalis (L.) **231,** 167
Populus alba L. 163
   P. x canadensis MOENCH
   var. serotina 164
P. nigra L. 164
P. n. var. italica DUROI 164
P. tremula L. 163
Potato 172
Potato cancer 172
Potentilla erecta (L.) RÄUSCH
   131
P. reptans L. 131
Prickly buckler-fern 113
Prosopis pectoralis (FÖRST.)
   183
Prunus amygdalus BATSCH
   135
P. avium (L.) 136
P. cerasus L. 136
P. domestica L. var. domes-
   tica B. & S. 135
P. d. var. insititia (L.)
   POIRET 135
P. padus L. 135, 136
P. persica (L.) BATSCH 135
P. p. var. nectarina (AIT.)
   MAXIM. 135
P. spinosa L. 135
Pseudocone gall **25, 26,** 114
Pseudomonas tumefaciens
   (MIG.) 118

Pseudotsuga taxifolia
   (POIRET) BRITT. 114
Psylla buxi L. **78,** 126
Psyllopsis fraxini L. **247–8,**
   172
Pteridium aquilinum (L.)
   KUHN 113
Pteromalus SWEDERUS 183
Puccinia graminis PERS.
   34–8, 116
P. *lagenophorae* COOKE.
   272–3, 178
P. malvacearum MONT.
   39, 117
P. suaveolens PERS. 178
P. terrieriana MAYOR
   272–273, 178
Purples gall 183
Purple willow 169
Purse gall **215,** 164
Puss-moth 164
Pyrus communis L. 115, 137

Quercus cerris L. 155
Q. petraea (MATT.)
   LIEBEL. 149
Q. robur L. 149

Raestelia lacerata SOWERBY
   115
Ranunculus repens L. 116
Raphanus raphaniastrum L.
   119
Raspberry 131
Red barnacle gall **172,** 157
beet 173
currant 139, 141
deadnettle 139
pea gall **180,** 159
wart gall **181,** 159
whortleberry 170
Reversion 139
Rhabdophaga heterobia F.
   LÖW **224,** 168, 169
   R. rosaria (H. LÖW) **233–
   234,** 167, 169
   R. salicis SCHRB. **235,** 169
Rhizobium beyerinckii (FR.)
   52, 14, 25, 126
   R. radicicola (FR.) **53,** 14,
   25, 126, 145
Rhodites eglanteriae HTG. 132
   R. nervosus (CURT.) 132
   R. rosae HTG. 132, 133
   R. rosarum GIR. 132
Rhododendron 171
Rhopalomyia millefolii H.
   LÖW **277,** 179
Rhynchaenus quercus (L.)
   126
Rhytisma acerinum FR. **3,** 13
Ribbon-footed corn-fly 184
Ribes nigrum L. 138
   R. rubrum agg. 139, 141
Ribwort plantain 176
Robin's pincushion 133
Root gall (oak) **163,** 151
Root-nodules **52, 53,** 126

Rorippa sylvestris (L.) BESSER
   120
Rosa arvensis HUDS. 132
   R. canina L. 132, 133, 135
   R. pimpinellifolia L. 133
Round-headed rampion 176
Rubus caesius L. 130
   R. fruticosus agg. 130
   R. idaeus L. 131
Ruby-tailed wasp 183
Rumex acetosella agg. 176

Sacciphantes abietis RUR. 114
Salix alba L. 167, 169
   S. atrocinerea BROT. 169
   S. aurita L. 169
   S. caprea L. 166, 169
   S. cinerea L. 169
   S. fragilis L. 168
   S. matsudana KOIDZUMI
   var. tortuosa **6**
   S. purpurea L. 169
   S. triandra L. 168
   S. viminalis L. 167
Saperda populnea L. **223,**
   27, 166
Sarothamnus scoparius (L.)
   WIMMER 128
Scabiosa columbaria L. 14, 178
Schenck's gall **206–7,** 162
Schinzia alni WORON. 145
Schizomyia pimpinellae F. LÖW
   140
Schizoneura lanuginosa
   (HTG.) **137,** 141
   S. lanigerum (HAUS.) 138
   S. ulmi (L.) 141
Sciara tilicola H. LÖW 123
Scots pine 115, 178
Scrophularia aquatica L. 174
   S. nodosa L. 174
Semiaphis atriplicis (L.) **47,**
   121
Senecio aquaticus HILL 178
   S. cineraria DC. 178
   S. erucifolius L. 178
   S. jacobaea L. 178
   S. squalidus L. 178
   S. vulgaris L. 178
Sessile oak 149
Sheep's sorrel 176
Shepherd's purse 120
Sidalcea A. GRAY 117
Silk-button spangle gall **194–5,**
   201, 161
Silver birch 138, 142, 144
Silver fir 114, 170
Sinapis arvensis L. 119
Sisymbrium officinale (L.)
   SCOP. 120
Sitka spruce 114
Sitona GERMAR 127
Sium latifolium L. 165
Slime-fungus 119, 145
Small scabious 14, 178
Smooth pea-gall **97,** 132
Smooth spangle gall **196–7, 205,**
   162

Soft rush 182
Solanum dulcamara L. 173
  S. nigra L. 173
  S. tuberosum L. 172
Sonchus arvensis L. 164, 181
  S. oleraceus L. 164, 181
Sorbus aria (L.) CRANTZ 137
  S. aucuparia L. 115, 137
Sour cherry 136
Sow-thistle 164
Spathegaster albipes SCHENCK 162
  S. baccarum L. 161
  S. flosculi GIR. 159
  S. giraudi TSCHEK 159
  S. interruptor HTG. 161
  S. similis ADLER 160
  S. taschenbergi (SCHLECH.) 159
  S. tricolor SCHENCK 162
  S. varius SCHENCK 162
  S. verrucosa (SCHLECH.) 159
  S. vesicatrix SCHLECH. 161
Speedwell 136
Spiked pea-gall **98**, 133
Spilonota aceriana MANN. 163
Spiral gall **217–18**, 165
Stachys sylvatica L. 139
Starved plum 135
Stellaria L. 114
Stilt-legged fly 127
Stinging nettle 140, 141
Strawberry 130
Striped gall **186**, 160
Swede 118, 119
Sweet violet 130
Swine cress 120
Sycamore 125
Sycamore leaf-blotch **3**
Synchitrium endobioticum (SCHILB.) PERCIVAL **54**, 14, 173
Syndiplosis petioli (KIEF.) **213–14**, 163

Taphrina aurea (FR.) 166
  T. betulina ROSTR. 142, 146
  T. carpini (FR.) 146
  T. deformans (BERK.) TUL. **106**, 135
  T. populina FR. 162
  T. pruni (FUCKEL) TUL. **104–5**, 135
  T. turgida (ROSTR.) 142, 144, 146
Taraxacum officinale WEBER 171
Tassel gall **288**, 182

Taxomyia taxi (INCH.) **32–3**, 116, 128
Taxus baccata L. 116
Tephritis bardanae SCHRANK **278**, 180
Terminal rosette gall 169
Tetraneura ulmi DE GEER **138**, 142
Tetrastichus eriophyes TAYLOR 148
Thecabius affinis (KALT.) **217**, 165
Thuja occidentalis L. **5**
Thymus serpyllum L. 175
Tilia x vulgaris L. 121
Timberman beetle 166
Toadflax 174
Tomato 173
Tortrix icterana (FRÖL.) 176
  T. paleana (HUB.) **265**, 176
Torymus bedeguaris (L.) 134
Tragopogon pratensis L. 182
Treacle mustard 120
Tree mallow 117
Trifolium repens L. 127
Trigonaspis megaptera (PANZ.) **208–9**, 163
  T. renum HTG. 163
Trioza urticae L. **132**, 140
Triticum aestivum L. 116, 183
  T. turgidum L. 116, 183
Truffle gall **178**, 158
Trypeta bardanae SCHRANK 180
  T. cardui WALK. 180
  T. solstitialis WALK. 180
Turnip 119
Turnip-and-cabbage gall-weevil **50**, 119
Turkey oak 154
Twig gall **174**, 157
Twist disease 184
Tylenchus devastatrix KUHN **88**, 130, 179
  T. millefolii F. LÖW 179
  T. dipsaci 130
  T. scandens BAST. 183
  T. tritici ROFR. **293**, 183
Tylos corrigiolatus L. 127
Typhlodromus pyri SCHEUT. 137

Ulmus glabra HUDS. 141
  U. procera SALIS. 141
Upright goosefoot 126
Urocystis pompholygodes LÉV. **40**, 116
Urophlyctis leproides TRB. 173
Urophora cardui (L.) 180
  U. solstitialis (L.) 180

Urtica dioica L. 140

Vaccinium vitis-idaea L. 170
Veronica anagallis-aquatica L. 174
  V. beccabunga L. 174
  V. chamaedrys 173
Viburnum lantana L. 176
Vicia sativa L. 129
  V. sepium L. 129
Viola odorata L. 130
Violet-egg gall **183**, 159

Wachtiella persicariae (L.) **130–1**, 140
  W. rosarum (HARDY) **95**, 128, 132
Walnut 142
Water betony 174
Water speedwell 174
Wayfaring-tree 177
Wheat 116, 183
White beam 137
White beet 173
  blister 120
  clover 127, 128
  deadnettle 139
  mould of Cruciferae 120
  poplar 163, 165, 166
  willow 167, 168, 169
Whooping gall **31**, 116
Wild carrot 140
  parsnip 140
  radish 119, 120
  thyme 175
Witches-broom **4**, **23**, **24**, 114, 142, 143, 146, 147
Wood anemone 116
  blue-grass 183
  burdock 180
  woundwort 139
Woody nightshade 173
Woolly aphid 138
Woolly gall 156
Wych elm 141

Xestophanes brevitarsis (THOM.) 131
  X. potentillae (RETZ.) **90**, 131
  X. tormentillae SCHLECH. 131

Yarrow 179
Yellow rocket 120
Yew 116

Zygobia carpini (F. LÖW) **142**, 146